Pioneer Astronomers

PIONEER
ASTRONOMERS

NAVIN
SULLIVAN

Drawings by Eric Fraser

ATHENEUM 1967 NEW YORK

ACKNOWLEDGMENT

The author is most grateful to Colin A. Ronan, Director
of the Historical Section of the British Astronomical
Association, and to Ivan King, Associate Professor of
Astronomy at the University of Illinois, for their helpful
comments on the manuscript of this book.

To the memory of
MY FATHER
who introduced me to science

Preface

In this book I have tried to explain a little of the way in which men have explored the universe. When men had no telescopes, they believed that the universe was a fairly small and simple place, and that they were the most important part of it. Today we know that the universe is very large and very diverse, and we think differently about ourselves.

I have not dealt with all the different kinds of work that astronomers do. Instead, I have singled out pioneers who helped us to explore farther and farther into the universe. As you will see, each step they took depended on one taken by someone else before. And at each step they found that there was more and more to explore. Today, we know that astronomy, the oldest of the sciences, is only just beginning.

Contents

Handwritten annotations: proved Newtons law · sun's spectrum found different minerals had spectrums · spiral galaxies took pictures with huge telescope · I LIKE pg. 149

Pioneer Astronomers

COPERNICUS

MARIA DA NOVARA, professor of astronomy, looked around at his new students. It was the fall of 1496 and the beginning of an academic year. His students had come from many countries, for the University of Bologna was one of the greatest in Europe. Among them was a freshman from the borderland between Germany and Poland. His name was Nicholas Koppernigk or, in the Latin preferred by scholars, Copernicus.

As Novara prepared to speak, Copernicus leaned forward eagerly. He was interested in astronomy.

"It is generally believed," said Novara, "that the Earth is a globe standing still at the center of the universe. Around it move the Moon, the Sun, and the five planets. Beyond these, but still quite near, are the stars, turning on a transparent sphere. We are therefore at the very center of the universe, and everything revolves around us."

Novara went on to explain that the planets appeared each night in a different place against the pattern of stars. They slowly wandered eastward, but at intervals they would pause and move backward for a while, after which they would resume their eastward journey. For some reason they traced out loops in the heavens.

"This was explained over 1300 years ago by the great Greek mathematician Ptolemy," said Novara. "He said that all heavenly bodies must move in circles, because the circle is the most perfect geometrical form, and heavenly bodies must be perfect. Now since the planets move in loops, they evidently cannot travel in simple circles. However, Ptolemy figured that the loops are a combination of small circles moving around in large circles. Thus the planets go around in a series of circles-upon-circles. By using a total of 39 different circles, Ptolemy and his followers were able to explain the movements of the Moon, the Sun, and the five planets."

Copernicus wrinkled his nose suspiciously. He knew that Ptolemy's ideas were important. They had seemed to work for over 1000 years. In fact, Columbus had used them successfully when navigating his way to the New World. All the same Copernicus could not help thinking that 39 circles were a lot to explain how only seven bodies moved.

"There ought to be some simpler explanation," he told himself.

As he continued with his studies, Copernicus learned how to make astronomical observations with the instruments of the time. Novara taught his students the use of the triquetrum, for measuring the heights of the stars in the sky. There was the Jacob's Staff, for gauging the angle between two stars. For noting the height of the noonday sun, he showed them the plinth, which Ptolemy had invented. None of these instruments was any better than those used over a thousand years earlier. Copernicus felt dissatisfied with a science in which nothing ever seemed to change.

One day he asked Novara whether men had ever had any other ideas about astronomy. Novara was delighted.

"Yes," he said. "My teacher, the famous Regiomontanus, never liked Ptolemy's system. He preferred the ideas of another ancient Greek, Aristarchus of Samos. According to Aristarchus, the Sun only appears to move across the sky each day and around the other side of the Earth at night. Instead, he thought that the Earth turns on its axis like a top, carrying us from sunlight to darkness to sunlight again. This spinning would also make the stars seem to move across the sky each night. What is more, Aristarchus believed that the Earth went in a great circle around the Sun each year!"

"But if the Earth were spinning around, we would be thrown off!" protested Copernicus. "And when a stone is thrown up in the air, it should be left behind."

Novara could not explain this. All he could suggest was that everything on the Earth might be carried round in some kind of protecting envelope of air.

"I do not know which explanation is correct," he confessed. "But I believe that the geometry of the skies should be simple. Whichever idea is the more simple is probably the right one."

Copernicus listened eagerly. Here was someone

who, like himself, suspected complicated explanations. Maybe, then, he was right to question the ideas of the great Ptolemy!

Copernicus plunged deeper into his studies of astronomy, with Novara encouraging him. He learned Greek and read Ptolemy in the original, sitting up half the night to wrestle with the circles. His brother, Andreas, came battering at his door, urging him to leave his books and enjoy himself, but Nicolas shook his head. He was enjoying himself too much where he was. The ideas of Aristarchus had kindled his imagination, and he was determined to see where they led.

But he had to study other subjects, too. He learned the geometry he needed before he could fully master Ptolemy's ideas. He learned the outlandish medicine of the time, jotting prescriptions down on whatever was handy, even on the back of his textbook of Euclid.

"Take lizards in olive oil," he noted solemnly, "and earthworms in wine. . . ." He might have ideas of his own in astronomy, but in medicine he was content to follow others.

Now officially a Canon of the Church, thanks to unscrupulous string-pulling by his uncle who was a bishop, Copernicus also studied church law. From Bologna he went to Rome; from Rome he went to Padua. Basking under the sunny Italian sky, he thought with a shudder of his gloomy northern homeland.

But at last, in 1506, he had to leave. His uncle, the Bishop of Ermland, summoned him to be his private physician. Sorrowfully, Copernicus packed up and said good-by to Italy, realizing that his student days were over. It was about time: he was 33 years old.

Living in the Bishop's official residence, Heilsberg Castle, Copernicus had to observe elaborate formalities. At noon, the dinner bell sounded and all the castle residents had to come to the doors of their apartments and wait respectfully for the Bishop. Then, to the sound of the baying hounds he had just fed, the Bishop would appear in the courtyard, splendidly dressed in miter and purple gloves, and carrying his staff of office. Everyone would follow him to the Hall of Knights, where each had his place at a table, strictly allocated according to social rank. The Bishop naturally sat at the principal table. Copernicus, as his nephew and physician, sat at the second. The ninth table, which was the bottom of the scale, was reserved for jugglers, jesters, and other entertainers.

It was in these strange surroundings that Copernicus struggled to reform astronomy and alter the whole picture men had of themselves in the universe. He was like a revolutionary secretly trying to make a bomb that would blow everything upside-down, but instead of explosives his bomb was filled with ideas.

During the six years he spent at Heilsberg Castle, Copernicus became convinced that the Earth did indeed go around the Sun. This explained away the planetary loops. He had found some of the simplicity he had longed for!

"The Earth takes a year to go around the Sun," he told himself, "but Mars takes two years and Jupiter nearly twelve. Surely, then, as the Earth rushes round and round, it will regularly pass by these slower-moving planets. And every time that it overtakes one of them, that planet will go backward for a while, in relation to the Earth."

It was a brilliantly simple idea. Like many great ideas, it may now seem obvious, but when Copernicus was thinking of it, it was difficult to imagine. Nowadays we know that if we look out of a train in which we are passing a train on the next track, that slower train often seems to be going backward. Later, however, when we are well past, we see it from a distance and realize that it is going forward.

"Only suppose that the Earth is moving, and we can explain the planetary loops as an illusion," Copernicus noted with triumph.

Once he accepted that the Earth went around the Sun, he was ready to believe that it spun round like a top as well. Some men argued that if it spun fast enough to turn around once in a day, it would shiver into pieces like a wooden wheel that was spun too fast. Copernicus countered this by reasoning that if the great sphere carrying the stars revolved instead, it would have to go much faster and be all the more likely to break apart. All the same, the speed at which the Earth must turn was frightening.

"We are all spinning around at 150 double paces every second!" he breathed, hardly daring to grasp the fact. If he were looking on, from a distance, everything would go flashing by in the blink of an eye. And he could not explain why everything was not thrown off the Earth; he never thought of the Earth's gravity as a safe anchor on this ride through space.

There was another puzzle, too. Aristarchus had made a rough measurement of how far the Sun must be from the Earth. Using crude data, he had figured that it was at least 4 or 5 million miles away. (Actually it is 93 million.) If the Earth went round the Sun, this meant that it must travel in a gigantic circuit some 10 million miles across. But as men believed the stars were not far away, they correctly argued that such a tremendous journey would surely bring the Earth close to the stars, first on one side of the circuit, then on another. However, no one could see groups of stars looking nearer at one part of the year than at another. This proved, they decided, that the Earth was not moving round the Sun.

Copernicus, however, saw things differently.

"It proves instead that the stars must be very far away . . . much farther than anyone has imagined," he stated. "In fact, they must be so far away that even a journey of 10 million miles is trifling in comparison, and the distance between us and them remains almost the same!"

Copernicus was bold enough to imagine a universe very different from the one he had been brought up to believe in. Instead of being tranquilly at rest, the Earth was whirling at a terrible speed round the central Sun. The familiar stars, that looked so near, were planted on their sphere far out in the deeps of space.

However, although he had explained away the planetary loops, Copernicus still could not explain the planetary orbits as simple circles. His observations showed that they were not. He therefore clung to the basic idea of circles-upon-circles. His planets not only orbited the sun in concentric circles, but also went around in smaller circles, rotating on their axes as they did so. To justify this, he had to insure the fact that these movements gibed with all the observations men had made of the positions of the planets. This meant checking every possible arrangement of circles-upon-circles against thousands of records piled up by ancient astronomers.

Gradually, he thought he could see that his calculations would work out. Unable to keep the news to himself any longer, he began dropping hints to favored visitors at the castle. Finally, in 1512 he wrote a short book explaining the general scheme of his ideas, but omitting any detailed mathematics. He sent a few handwritten copies of this book privately to various scholars.

"Thirty-four circles," he wrote proudly, "suffice to explain the entire structure of the universe and the entire ballet of the planets."

Unfortunately, Copernicus still had to complete the detailed calculations. He found to his dismay that the longer he worked at them, the more complicated they became. Circles were piled on circles in nightmarish profusion. In the end, after no fewer than twenty years of struggling, he found that he needed 48 circles—nine *more* than Ptolemy had used! It was a bitter disappointment. No longer sure of his theory, he locked his manuscript away and did not try to publish it.

Meanwhile, his short handwritten book had been read by scholars in different parts of Europe. One, a young professor named Joachim Rheticus, was so enthusiastic about it that he came to see the aging astronomer. He brought precious gifts of first printed editions of Euclid and Ptolemy in Greek. More important, he brought boundless energy and belief in Copernicus and his ideas.

"My teacher," he declared, "your system will open a new era in astronomy. You must publish your book, for the good of mankind!"

Copernicus was not so sure. The nightmarish arrangement of circles haunted him. But young Rheticus would not give in. Day after day he argued and pleaded. He even offered to go through the manuscript for stray errors and then to arrange for the printing. Anything, if only Copernicus would agree!

And eventually Copernicus yielded. He took the bulky manuscript out of its hiding place and handed it over to his enthusiastic disciple. In 1543 it was published under the title *On the Revolutions of the Heavenly Spheres*. But its author had waited too long to see how it was received. At the end of 1542 he had a stroke, and when the first copy was brought to him he was at the end of his strength. He touched it, and that was all. A few hours later he was dead. It was May 24, 1543.

Copernicus was right to be worried about his complicated system of circles. We now know that, although the Earth does go round the Sun, the additional circles are not needed to explain its movements or those of the planets.

Yet in spite of his failure, Copernicus succeeded. He was the first man to try to show, precisely and mathematically, how the Earth might move around the Sun, and his explanation of the planetary loops holds good today. More important still, he helped people to believe in the idea of a moving Earth. Maybe it moved in circles-upon-circles, maybe it didn't—but at any rate it moved! Man was no longer the center of the universe. And once that was accepted, the way was open for someone to start finding out how the Earth really does travel.

KEPLER

In 1596 an unknown German mathematics teacher named Johannes Kepler wrote a book that startled scholars everywhere.

"Copernicus was wrong," he declared. "The planets move in simple circles round the Sun. And I have discovered a beautiful mathematical scheme that explains the distances between these circles."

The idea had come to Kepler one day while standing at the blackboard. It struck him with such force that he was sure it must be true. The distances between the orbits of the planets had been calculated by Copernicus in ratios, not actual distances. And although these ratios did not fit exactly into Kepler's scheme, he was sure it was not his fault.

"It is because Copernicus used faulty observations

in his calculations," claimed the young mathematician
boldly. "With accurate observations, I shall be able to
show that my scheme is correct."

He knew that the most accurate observations in the
world were being made by a Danish nobleman named
Tycho Brahe. This astronomer had built an observatory
on his private island of Hveen, off the Danish coast.

Kepler yearned to get hold of Tycho's observations.

However, he was a poor teacher living at Gratz, in
Austria. He could not afford to go all the way to Den-
mark. Sorrowfully, he decided that he would never be
able to check his theory.

And then, in 1597, Tycho Brahe quarreled with the
Danish king. As a result, he packed up and left Hveen,
taking all his instruments with him. For two years he
roamed about Europe and finally, in 1599, he settled
down in Prague as official astronomer to Rudolph II,
Emperor of Bohemia.

When Kepler heard of this he was overjoyed.
Prague was near enough for him to be able to go there.
At last he would be able to study Tycho's observations.

"With his observations, I shall build a new model of
the Solar System," he told his wife Barbara.

Luckily, Baron Hoffman, Councillor to the Emperor, was in Gratz. The hard-up mathematics teacher
begged a ride in his coach, and on January 1, 1600, the
journey began.

It was the first day of a new century. For Kepler, it
was the first day of a new life.

The two men met on February 4th at Brahe's observatory in the Castle of Benatek, near Prague. Kepler
was a thin, shabbily dressed young man with melan-

choly, short-sighted eyes. Brahe was a splendidly dressed man with a bald head and large, curled mustaches. More striking still, he had a false nose because his real one had been cut off in a duel. Brahe had made the new nose himself out of gold and silver alloy. It shone in the light and Kepler could not help staring curiously at it.

"I do not receive you as a guest, but as a very welcome friend and colleague in the contemplation of the skies," said Brahe grandly.

He showed Kepler the instruments with which he made observations ten times more accurate than those known to Copernicus. There were giant wood and metal sextants. There was a brass quadrant, 14 feet in diameter, for gauging the heights of stars or planets. Most splendid of all, there was Brahe's special pride, a great equatorial armillary with which he measured the angles between stars or stars and planets. And engraved on a magnificent brass globe were the results of his observations—the positions of a thousand stars.

Kepler blinked in astonishment. The globe alone was worth 80 years of his salary. The splendor of Brahe's equipment was beyond anything he had imagined. At the thought of the work that had gone into recording those one thousand positions, he began to see what might lie ahead of him if he were to try to produce an exact astronomy. He could hardly wait to get his hands on the precious data Brahe had so laboriously collected.

"You must have many books full of observations," he murmured. "When may I examine these?"

To his dismay, Brahe began to look secretive. "Oh, as to that, we shall see," he replied. "There is no hurry."

Brahe knew very well what the young mathematician wanted, but the observations had cost so much effort that he could not easily give them away.

Kepler saw that the great astronomer wished to hoard his precious data. It was a great disappointment. After coming all the way from Gratz, his home and his wife, was he to be left empty-handed?

Kepler followed the imperious Dane about the castle. He saw the positions where observations were taken, and he met the senior assistant, Longomontanus.

"Longomontanus has been studying the orbit of Mars," Tycho Brahe said. "He is having difficulties with it. Mars seems more unpredictable than the other planets."

He went on to explain that the other planets seemed to move pretty well in circles, which was how they believed all the planets moved, but the circle for Mars had not so far been plotted.

For the next few weeks Kepler tried to get details about the planetary movements out of Brahe. His eagerness was obvious, but the astronomer would do no more than mention a figure here and there in passing. Kepler ground his teeth and waited doggedly, hoping that he might yet persuade this miserly Dane to change his mind.

And then one day Brahe called him into the study.

"As I told you," he said, "Longomontanus has been having trouble with Mars." He paused, eyeing Kepler. Taking out the box of ointment he always carried, he thoughtly rubbed some ointment on his metal nose.

"I have decided to assign him to the Moon instead," he announced. "Will you take over Mars?"

Kepler started joyfully. If he took over work on Mars, Brahe would have to disgorge all his observations for the planet!

"Give me eight days," he cried, "and I will solve its orbit!"

But he did not solve it in eight days. For the next eighteen months, he slaved away at the orbit of Mars and still did not succeed. Meantime, he had also to take on various chores for Brahe, tedious, time-wasting work that he hated.

Nor did he get data about other planets. As he had expected, Brahe gave out the Mars data, but with the rest he was as secretive as ever. At dinner Kepler was tantalized with scraps of information which Brahe threw at him like so many bones to a dog. Once, unable to bear it any longer, Kepler fled to Prague and stayed with the kindly Baron Hoffman, but Brahe persuaded him to return.

And then, on October 13, 1601, the great astronomer fell sick after a banquet, and eleven days later he died. In a delirium on his death bed, he kept repeating: "Let me not seem to have lived in vain."

A fortnight afterward, Johannes Kepler was officially appointed Brahe's successor. At last he could have all the data to work on.

However, he went right on trying to solve the orbit for Mars. A lot of data was available for this planet, and besides he was too immersed in the problem to quit working on it.

"Assuming that Mars moves in a circle round the Sun, the difficulty is to find the circle corresponding with the observations," he mused.

He knew already that Mars was not always at the same distance from the Sun. The Sun was not at the center of the circle. He also knew that the speed of Mars varied: the nearer it was to the Sun, the faster it moved.

Kepler supposed that some force was needed to

keep a planet circling the Sun. He guessed that this force might come from the Sun and push the planet on its way. Of course he had no idea what the force might be.

"If the force spreads out from the Sun, it will grow weaker as it travels farther away," he told himself. "In other words, it will have less push on a planet when it is farther from the Sun, and more push when it is nearer. This could explain why Mars changes speed, going faster when it is nearer the Sun!"

Enthusiastically, Kepler set about trying to fit Brahe's observations to this idea. Sifting through the mass of data, he selected four key observations and tried to fit a circle to them. Many circles were possible and every time he tried one he had to check it against all the other observations for Mars.

It was a tremendous job. Only someone as untiring as Kepler would have stuck at it. He made over 70 trials and covered 900 pages with calculations in his small handwriting. At last, after several years of work, he found a circle that seemed to fit, allowing for the fact that even Brahe's observations might not be accurate within two minutes of arc. (One minute of arc is the same as the width of the head of a pin seen from about 5 yards away.) He was overjoyed.

"One more test," he whispered, driven by his relentless thoroughness. Turning to the records, he chose two rare observations and confidently tested his circle against them.

To his consternation, they did not fit. They were way out, by as much as eight minutes of arc! He knew that Brahe would never slip up that much, so there was no help for it—the circle was wrong! Kepler groaned and tore at his hair. All his work was wasted; he would have to start again.

And start again he did, with truly heroic courage and persistence.

"Those eight minutes," he wrote, "point the way to a complete reformation of astronomy."

He had lost faith in circular orbits and saw that he must try some fresh approach. He was determined to obey the facts, the wonderfully exact observations collected by the old Dane. No theory was any good unless it accounted for all of them.

A wild, improbable idea came to him. "Maybe an oval would fit," he muttered, thinking of the shape of a hen's egg.

He plunged into fresh calculations. Thousands were needed to check the idea. On July 4, 1603, he wrote to a friend that he could not solve the geometrical problems of the oval.

"If only," he added, "the shape were a perfect ellipse."

Yet he went on struggling with the egg-shaped oval for several more months, until finally he had to admit himself beaten. It was then that he decided not to start with any fixed idea of what shape the orbit might be but to let the observations speak for themselves.

Very carefully, he put down twenty of the points of the orbit.

"They surely fit some kind of an oval," he muttered, staring at them. "But the shape is like a circle too . . . maybe between the two, like a circle flattened a little at two opposite sides . . ."

It was around Easter, 1605, when he had this inspiration and soon all the figures fell into place. Just as he had wished in his letter two years earlier, the orbit really was a perfect ellipse. He had solved the orbit of Mars at last—not after eight days as he had once boasted, but he had solved it all the same. And in his triumph he drew a little sketch beside his proof, showing the goddess of victory riding in her chariot over the clouds.

It is no wonder that the planetary orbits were for so long thought to be circles. As Kepler found with Mars, and went on to discover for the other known planets (including Earth), the orbits are all ellipses, but ellipses that are very nearly circles. And the Sun is in one focus of each ellipse.

But *why* are the orbits elliptical? *Why* do the planets travel at shifting speeds, accelerating as they near the Sun, decelerating as they draw away? And *why* do the outer planets travel more slowly than the inner ones, as even Copernicus had known? Kepler asked himself all these questions but he could not answer them. It was not until some 80 years later that an Englishman, Isaac Newton, showed that all these facts could be explained by one universal concept, gravity.

Before then, however, men were to have a better way of exploring the skies. The great quadrants and armillary spheres of which Tycho Brahe had been so proud were to be thrown away for ever. Instead, men were to use a marvelous new instrument, first devised by a humble eyeglass maker in Holland, and turned skyward by a brilliant Italian professor named Galileo Galilei. This was the telescope.

GALILEO

ONE MAY evening in 1609, a carriage rattled briskly through the streets of Padua, in Italy. In it was Galileo Galilei, professor of mathematics, returning from a trip to Venice. While he was there, he had received news from a former pupil named Jacques Badovere—news that had sent him hurrying home.

"A marvelous tube is on sale here," wrote Badovere, who was now living in Paris. "This tube makes distant objects appear close. A man two miles away can be seen distinctly. People call these tubes 'Dutch perspectives' or 'Dutch cylinders.' Some say that they were invented by Hans Lippershey, an obscure maker of eyeglasses in Middleburg, Holland. What is sure is that they employ two lenses, one convex and the other concave."

The carriage turned into the Borgo dei Vignali and

stopped outside Galileo's house. Pausing only to glance at his garden, Galileo hurried indoors and went to his study.

"One convex and one concave," he repeated as though in a trance. He drew writing paper toward him, dipped a sharpened quill in the ink, and began to draw.

"Suppose the convex lens is placed in front, to gather the light," he muttered. "Then if the concave lens is placed the right distance behind, it should magnify the gathered light."

He only had to figure the distance and he would be able to make one of these marvelous "Dutch perspectives" for himself! He had already taken the precaution of bringing a good assortment of eyeglass lenses from Venice.

By the time that Galileo went to bed he felt fairly sure that he had solved the problem. Early the next morning he hurried to his workshop. The place was filled with gadgets he had already invented, including an apparatus for indicating temperature and another for timing the pulse of a patient. Now he would make a tube to demolish distance.

Seizing a handy piece of lead tubing, he cut it down to the length he wanted. Then he took a convex lens and placed it in one end, and placed a concave lens in the other. Excitedly, he held the tube to his eye and peered through. Immediately he gave a cry of delight. It worked! The church tower several streets away might have been just outside.

How much did his tube magnify? Galileo cut different-sized circles of paper and pinned them up on a wall. When he found that his tube made a small circle look the size of a larger one seen with the naked eye, he could figure the magnification by comparing the actual sizes of the circles. In this way he found that his telescope magnified three times.

Proudly he sat down and wrote to his friends in Venice telling them of his success. Then, after getting the lenses mounted in a more imposing tube made of wood, he hurried back to Venice himself. The Venetians were famous as sailors and navigators. This tube would show them ships out at sea long before they could be seen with the naked eye. Surely, thought Galileo, the nobles of Venice would pay well for such a device.

His thinking was right. On August 8, 1609, even the aged members of the Venetian Senate clambered painfully up to the very top of the tower of St. Mark's Cathedral, the highest building in Venice. There they gazed out to sea through Galileo's primitive telescope and, to their delight, found that they could see ships sailing toward them a good two hours before they were visible with the naked eye. They promptly doubled Galileo's salary as professor of mathematics which, although he was at the University of Padua, was controlled by them.

Galileo returned triumphantly to Padua and disappeared into his workshop. Already he was planning better lenses and longer tubes. He intended to teach himself lens grinding. He dreamed of magnifications of 8, 20, even 30!

And when he had made these telescopes, he was going to use them to look not at the sea but the sky. Five years earlier, all Padua had seen an extraordinary happening: a new star had appeared in the sky. (Kepler had seen it too, and had pointed out that evidently the stars were not unchanging, as men then believed.) Like everyone else, Galileo had been surprised and puzzled by the new star. Now he promised himself that he was going to look more closely at the heavens.

It was four days after new moon. Galileo's newest telescope, magnifying 30 times, was resting in its cradle on a tripod stand. He squinted through it at the bright crescent, then drew what he saw by the light of a flickering candle.

The Moon was, he knew, lit from one side by the Sun. He noticed that the boundary between light and dark on the Moon's surface was wavy and uneven. Also, he saw bright spots of light dotted over the dark area. what could they be?

He puzzled over them for a while, and then he made a bold deduction.

"These spots of light are mountain peaks just catching the sunlight," he decided. "And the wavy line at the boundary between light and dark exists because there are mountains there, too. It is sunrise up there and, just as on Earth at dawn, the mountain peaks are bathed in sunlight while the valleys are still dark." It seemed incredible. Yet it must be true. There were mountains on the Moon, as there were on Earth!

Until then no one had seriously supposed that the Moon might be something like the Earth. People had thought of the Moon and planets as heavenly bodies, things quite different in kind from the Earth.

How high were the mountains? Galileo could not measure them directly, but he devised a way of comparing them with the diameter of the Moon, which was fairly accurately known. When he had worked out the figures, he could hardly believe them. The Moon mountains proved to be enormous, much higher than earthly mountains: up to four miles high.

It was a whole new world that Galileo was looking at. But was it full of living creatures or was it dead? He wondered if there was air on it, and shuddered at the idea that it might be cold and silent, a dead world forever circling the Earth.

Then he began to explore the sky. Night after night he gazed upward, and what he found was a revelation. With the naked eye only about 2,000 stars are visible at any one time. Even with his relatively low-power telescope, Galileo found myriads more than that.

He examined the belt and sword of Orion: instead of the usual nine stars he found 89! The constellation of the Pleiades, in which sharp-eyed observers could only see seven stars, became a swarm of 43. As for the Milky Way—it was impossible to think of counting the stars in it. Wherever Galileo looked, his telescope showed crowded clusters of stars.

"Many of them are tolerably large and extremely bright," he noted, "but the number of small ones is quite beyond determination."

On January 7, 1610, while he was gazing at the sky an hour after sunset, he noticed that the planet Jupiter was visible. Immediately he turned his telescope onto it, eager to examine one of the planets for the first time.

He saw that it was a small, round disk that did not sparkle like a star. Peering more closely, he saw something else: three bright little points of light were grouped near it, two to the east of Jupiter, one to the west:

(East)   x   x O   x   (West)

At first he told himself that these bright points must be three fixed stars. But the next night, to his astonishment, they were differently grouped: all three were to the west of Jupiter.

(East)   O x x x   (West)

"Can Jupiter have moved past them?" Galileo asked himself in bewilderment. "If so, it is not traveling the way astronomers have always said it does."

He waited impatiently to look again the next night, but to his disappointment the sky was cloudy. However, the following night was clear. He rushed to his telescope and turned it with trembling hands toward Jupiter. This is what he saw:

(East)   x   x O   (West)

For a moment he wondered if he were going crazy. Now there were only two points of light, and both were to the east of Jupiter.

"Is Jupiter moving back and forth like a pendulum?" he muttered.

He searched the sky nearby, checking to see if Jupiter had moved in this way against the background of the fixed stars. It had not; it was on the course that astronomers had always charted for it.

"If Jupiter is not swinging to and fro, then the little points of light are," reasoned Galileo. "And since one of them has disappeared tonight, it is probably hidden by Jupiter—it has probably gone behind the planet. It looks as if these points of light are swinging *around* Jupiter!"

This meant that the points of light could not be

stars. To make sure that they were swinging around Jupiter, Galileo began a methodical series of observations.

On the next night, January 11th, he still saw only two of them, but now they had moved farther away from the planet. On the 12th they were closer again, and a third had appeared on the west of the planet. On the 13th, he had another surprise: there were four points of light.

(East)   x O x x x   (West)

He doubted no longer. "These are not fixed stars, but bodies belonging to Jupiter and going around it in various orbits," he decided. "Jupiter has four satellite moons of its own, just as the Earth has one!"

Full of excitement, he settled down to write a short account of all that he had discovered with his telescope. Two months later this was published in Venice, under the title *Messenger from the Stars*. His discoveries amazed the whole of Europe. Soon they were even being discussed in faraway Peking.

Galileo had opened up a new vision of the heavens. He had shown that the Moon is a rocky, mountainous globe, that the Earth is not unique in having a satellite moon, and that millions upon millions of stars exist. Soon he went further and discovered that Venus appears first as a crescent, then full, then dark, as it circles the Sun and reflects light at different angles. He even traced the movement of mysterious spots across the face of the Sun. The fact that the Sun has spots shocked some people, who felt that a celestial object ought to be without blemish. Galileo, however, was very interested, for the movement of the spots, in one direction, indicated that the Sun, like the Earth, was spinning round on its axis.

To many people this probing of the skies was exciting. They realized that for the first time men had a means of exploring space. But to others it was unsettling, even dangerous. This was because, although they were living 70 years after Copernicus, they still believed that the Earth did not move and was the center of the universe. The Church of Rome officially agreed with this belief, although some of its members did not.

Until now Galileo had not dared to defy the Church openly and declare that the Earth moved round the Sun.

"I would certainly dare to publish my ideas at once if more people like you existed," he had once written to Kepler. "Since they don't, I shall refrain from doing so."

However, his discoveries made Galileo a much more important man. He decided, finally, that the Church would not dare to curb him, and he began to state publicly that the Earth circled the Sun.

"Let them try to prove me wrong!" he exclaimed.

For some years the Roman Catholic Church let Galileo talk freely, only warning him from time to time, but many high officials of the Church remained unconvinced. And in fact, whatever Galileo said, he could not *prove* that the Earth goes round the Sun; he could only say, with Copernicus, that it seemed likely. (It was not until 1728 that conclusive proof was given by James Bradley, Third Astronomer Royal of England.)

In 1623 a new Pope was elected and the Church hardened against Galileo. He received more severe warnings than before, but would not give way. In 1632 he published a brilliant argument in favor of his beliefs, entitled *Dialogue on the Great World Systems.*

This was open defiance of the Church, and Galileo was summoned to appear before the Inquisition in Rome. Interrogation began on April 12, 1633. Galileo was asked to declare that he was wrong and that the Earth stood still. The questioning continued for a month.

The great astronomer was now seventy years old, and he was worn out by fatigue and by fear of the Inquisition. In the end, Galileo did as he was told. Never again did he say in public that the Earth moved.

Forbidden to concern himself with astronomy, Galileo now returned to an old interest of his: the study of how things move. And, although he did not suspect it, these studies were later to help in explaining just why the Earth does move.

Years before, he had shown that, contrary to all common sense, everything falls at the same speed, whatever its weight. He had actually dropped balls of different weights—some made of wood, some of lead—and found that they hit the ground at the same time. We now know that although a heavy weight is pulled more strongly by the Earth's gravity than a light weight, it needs that much more of a pull to move it downward at the same speed. Galileo knew nothing of the rules of gravity, but he did see that gravity moved the different weights at the same speed.

He had also found something more: as the weights fell, they moved faster and faster—they accelerated.

"If I can measure this acceleration, I shall be measuring how the Earth's gravity pulls," he told himself. He knew that the Earth's gravity must be a pull, or an attraction, because things always fall toward the Earth, not away from it. (Men had long thought of gravity in this way, but later Newton was to extend their ideas.)

Galileo believed that the pull of the Earth's gravity should make a falling object accelerate at a steady rate. Others before him had believed this. But he determined to prove it.

Ideally, he should have dropped things and measured just how they fell. The trouble was, they fell too fast for him to measure exactly. He needed to find a slower, but similar, movement that he could gauge precisely.

He thought of a ball rolling down a slope.

"Just as a ball falls downward because of gravity, so it rolls downward because of gravity," he reasoned. "Can I use the way it rolls as a guide to the way it falls?"

He decided that he could, and in the quiet villa near Florence where he now lived he began a series of experiments. Taking some very smooth wooden chutes, he rolled polished bronze balls down them and timed their progress. And he found that, however steep the slope, and however fast a ball rolled, the rate at which it increased its speed did indeed remain steady.

"This must mean that the pull of gravity is steady," he noted.

He knew just how fast the acceleration was for a ball rolling down a slope, but he did not know if the same acceleration would hold for a freely-falling ball. However, he was fairly sure that a freely-falling object would also accelerate at a steady rate. This was as far as he could go with his equipment. The exact value of the acceleration of a free-falling body was measured later by a great Dutch physicist named Christian Huygens.

Now Galileo began a different experiment. He let

a ball roll down one sloping board and up another board opposite. He found that the ball rolled up until it was level with the height from which it had started. He varied the slopes, but always got the same result. Even if the ball had to roll a greater distance upward than downward, it went on until it had reached its original height.

"The ball is like the weight on the end of a pendulum," he said, thoughtfully. "When released, it always goes up to the height from which it has started."

In his imagination he now played a trick on the ball. If it always tried to roll up to the height from which it had started, what would it do if it could never get up to that height? In other words, what if the opposite slope were not a slope at all, but level ground going on and on?

"If the ball can never reach the height from which it started, it ought to go on forever!"

Until then, men had always supposed that a continual force would be needed to keep something moving forever. Galileo, in an inspired moment, saw that this was not true. Once started in motion, an object could keep going on and on of its own accord. A force would be needed to stop it, not keep it moving.

This was a brilliant paradox of the kind that Galileo loved. Of course, he knew that in the real world a ball would not go on rolling forever, but it would be stopped by friction—which is a force.

Galileo called this tendency to keep moving inertia. The work expressed the idea that a moving object does not alter speed or direction unless it is forced to do so.

Satisfied with what he had learned, he went still further. In another imaginary experiment he combined what he had discovered about the pull of gravity with the idea of inertia.

"Suppose a cannon ball is fired out of a cannon," he muttered, drawing a diagram for himself. He knew the inertia of the moving ball would tend to make it keep going on in a straight line. Meanwhile, however, the Earth's gravity would be pulling the ball downward. How would the ball actually travel?

He figured out how the ball's tendency to go on in a straight line would combine with the pull on the ball from the Earth's gravity. The ball would, he found, travel in a special kind of curve called a parabola. How sharp this curve was would depend upon the speed of the ball when it was fired.

He could not test his idea by firing a cannon. However, he worked out a test that would give the same result. He took a wedge with a long, wide sloping side and started a ball rolling straight across the top of the sloping side. This was the firing of the cannon. But the ball, while going forward, also started to roll down the slope of the wedge. The forward movement and the downward movement were combined. And the route actually taken by the ball was, as he had prophesied, a parabola.

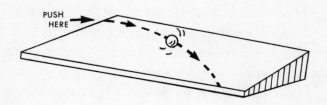

Galileo's test. He started the ball rolling straight across the top of the sloping side, and the route taken by the ball was a parabola.

Galileo's studies of rolling bronze balls had led him to the parabola, but he never imagined that this would help to explain why the planets travel as they do round the Sun.

Yet the ellipses of Kepler are closely related to the parabolas of Galileo. In 1642, the very year that Galileo died, the man who would prove this was born at Woolsthorpe in Lincolnshire, England. His name was Isaac Newton.

NEWTON

"Why do the planets go round the Sun?" Isaac Newton asked himself this question one summer day in 1666.

He was sitting in his garden. Behind him was the gray stone house in which he had grown up. Its walls still bore sundials which he had made as a boy. Indoors, his mother was preparing the evening meal. Her three younger children, Benjamin, Mary, and Hannah, were out in the fields of the farm helping with the harvest. However, she had long ago given up trying to turn Isaac into a farmer.

A year earlier, he had been studying at the University of Cambridge when a terrible plague had begun to strike in towns all over England. The university had sent its students home to avoid it. Now Newton was spending his time thinking and experimenting.

He did not ask himself why the planets moved, for he realized that they would keep going out of inertia. There was no friction in space to slow them down. But why did they move round and round, instead of going off in straight lines?

"Some force must be pulling them into closed orbits," he reasoned.

He remembered how, when he was a boy, he had used a sling to whirl a stone around before letting it fly. The cord of the sling had held the stone, pulling on it to stop it from flying off. Now it occurred to him that the pull on the planets did pretty much the same thing.

It was as though a cord from the Sun was pulling on the planets. But there were no cords up in the sky.

This mysterious pull was invisible, yet it had to be stronger than the toughest cord.

As Newton sat pondering, the wind, coming in gusts, swayed the branches of a tall apple tree that stood nearby. The branches were laden with ripe fruit and suddenly an apple was blown off one of them. With a thud, it landed some distance away.

The thud roused him, and he glanced around. Seeing the apple, he noted how far the wind had blown it. His mathematical mind instantly wondered why the apple had fallen just as it had. Why had it not fallen farther, or nearer?

The wind had hurled it forward; at the same time the Earth's gravity had pulled it downward. And like Galileo's cannon ball, it had traveled in a parabola. The distance it had gone had been set by the force of the wind.

Newton played with the idea. Suppose the wind were much, much stronger: how far would the apple travel then? Would it be blown right across Lincolnshire before it fell? Across the North Sea? How far?

By now Newton was not thinking about a real wind, but an imaginary one. He could make his imaginary wind as strong as he liked.

"With a fairly weak wind the apple would land, say, one mile away," he told himself. "Then, as it was hurled faster and faster, it would land farther and farther away—2, 5, 10, 100, and even 1,000 miles away."

As the distance increased, the parabola traveled by the apple would get larger and larger. Now Newton asked himself what sounded like an absurd question. What if the parabola became so big that it was larger than the curve of the Earth's surface?

"The apple would go in a curve round the Earth and come back to where it started," he decided. "With a large enough curve, the apple would never come down at all! It would keep going round and round the Earth."

Newton could not know that 300 years later men would launch artificial satellites into orbit round the Earth. But he realized that if his imaginary apple, or any other projectile, were moving fast enough it would go on and on round the Earth. The Earth's gravity would be pulling on it all the time, and so it would be "falling" all the time—but it would never hit the ground. We now know that such a projectile must travel at a minimum of 18,000 miles an hour. As long as it is outside the atmosphere, which would drag on it by friction, a satellite moving at this speed will keep circling endlessly around the Earth.

Newton was tremendously excited by his idea. He thought it through and then went on. If the Earth's gravity would hold a projectile in orbit, maybe it would hold the Moon in orbit, too. Maybe the pull of the Earth would operate even 238,000 miles away—the distance of the Moon from the Earth.

Might not gravity, pulling far across space, be the invisible cord he had been thinking of earlier? If the Earth pulled on the Moon, might not the Sun pull in the same way on the planets? Perhaps the pulls were of the same kind.

"Universal gravity," he whispered, imagining this strange, subtle attraction, acting throughout space so that every planet was affected by it. It was a prodigious vision. If only he could prove that it was correct!

Day after day Newton tussled with this gigantic problem. He had once partitioned off a part of a bedroom to make a little study, and had decorated it by drawing a pheasant and a nearby church on its walls. Now he sat here searching through his books and looking for clues.

"Kepler found that the farther a planet's orbit lies from the Sun, the more slowly the planet travels," he noted.

He examined the mathematical way Kepler had devised of stating this fact. By itself the fact explained nothing, but Newton began to take it to pieces to see what it really meant. Finally he saw that it gibed with the idea of a pull from the Sun which spread out in all directions, steadily growing weaker, just as light does.

This meant that the pull obeyed an inverse square law, already proved as a measure for centrifugal forces, getting weaker in proportion to the square of the distance. Two miles away it would be four times weaker than it was one mile away, while three miles away it would be nine times weaker, and so on.

If the Sun's gravity obeyed the inverse square law, then probably the Earth's gravity did too, Newton decided. But would the Earth's gravity, acting in this way, be strong enough to keep the Moon in orbit? Newton figured that the pull needed to keep the Moon in orbit had to make the Moon "fall" toward the Earth 0.0539 inch each second. Then he had to check to see whether the Earth's gravity would produce the necessary "fall" to do this.

To handle this calculation, he assumed that the center of the Earth. The moon, he figured on the basis of the later was just 60 times farther away from this center than was the surface of the Earth. By the inverse square law, the Earth's pull would be 60 x 60, or 3,600 times weaker at the Moon.

He knew that the pull at the Earth's surface was a little over 16 feet in a second. Dividing by 3,600 he found that the pull at the Moon came out at a "fall" of 0.0536 inch each second. This was only 0.6 per cent short of the necessary amount!

What Newton had done, of course, was only a rough calculation. He had made it simpler by pretending the Moon's orbit was a circle, not an ellipse. And he had yet to prove that he could assume the Earth's pull acted as though it came from the center of the Earth.

However, Newton now felt sure that gravity would explain the movements of the entire Solar System. Most scientists would have wanted to tell everyone of this tremendous discovery, but Newton said nothing. He was a shy and withdrawn person, who was content to keep his ideas to himself. Also, he may have felt that he should not announce his work until he had proved it in strict mathematical detail.

Whatever the reason, Newton now turned his attention to something quite different. Several years earlier, while he was at Cambridge, he had tried to make a better telescope than any so far devised. Galileo's telescopes, and bigger ones that other men had later developed, all had one important defect. Their lenses made things appear nearer, but they also made them appear fringed with colors. It was impossible to see stars or planets sharply and clearly in their real colors. Cheap opera glasses today have the same fault. Newton wanted to find out why these colors appeared. If he could do that, he reasoned, he might be able to devise a way of making better lenses which did not produce the unwanted colors.

He had already tried grinding lenses in different shapes, in the hope that a change of shape would give better results. It was laborious, finicky work, but he kept at it until he had tested every shape he could think of. None of them produced any real improvement.

"If the shape of the lens makes no difference, the glass of the lens must be the cause of the trouble," he decided.

He knew already that the same kind of color effect occurred when light passed through triangular glass prisms. These glint with all the colors of the rainbow. Prisms were sold as toys because people liked to see the colors, and Newton had once bought one at a fair. Now he began a careful series of experiments with glass prisms to see if he could find out just why the colors appeared.

At that time many people thought that white light —sunlight—was pure, basic light and that colored light was some kind of alteration of this. They thought that if sunlight shone through a piece of red stained glass in a church window it was somehow dyed red, rather as white cloth can be dyed. But the glass in a prism or a lens was not colored: why should colors appear there?

To get a small, easily managed beam of white light, Newton darkened his little study by covering the window with a shutter and then cutting a little hole in this shutter. He now had a thin shaft of sunlight slanting through the air into the darkened room. He put a white screen in the path of the beam, and a small round patch of light appeared on the screen. The next step was to find out what happened when a prism was placed in this shaft of sunlight.

He used a large prism on a metal stand, putting it carefully in the path of the light. The beam bent as it traveled through the prism and splayed out into colors. By using a lens, Newton was able to focus these colors sharply on the screen. To his delight, they stood out in beautiful, brilliant bands: red, orange, yellow, green, blue, and violet.

"Here are all the colors of the rainbow!" he exclaimed.

He moved the prism this way and that and found that the colors always appeared in the same order. Each color was bent at a particular angle by the prism. Violet light was bent, or refracted, most, then blue, and so on through the range to red, which was refracted least.

"Each color is bent differently, and so the beam of light is spread out by the prism," he noted.

Now he could see why telescope lenses did not show things clearly. To work properly, a lens must bend or refract light to one sharp focus. If the glass of the lens bent different colors by different amounts, they would not come to the same focus. The result would be a blurred picture ringed with color, just as actually occurred.

But what was this colored light? Was each color really white light "dyed" in some way?

"If it is dyed, another prism should alter it still further," he told himself.

To get only one color, he pierced a small hole in the screen where the red band struck it. Some of the red light now traveled on through the hole. He took a second prism and placed it in this shaft of red light.

The red light went through the prism, bending at the same angle that it had in the first prism, but it did not spread out and no other colors appeared.

"If the red light cannot be altered by a prism, maybe red is a basic kind of light—more basic than white light," Newton mused.

What about the other colors? He tried each in turn and found that they too stayed the same. There seemed to be no doubt that the color beams in the bands separated out by the prism were the fundamental kinds of light.

"Somehow white light must be a mixture of all these colors!" he decided.

It was an astonishing paradox, to think that whiteness was made by combining color. But Newton proved it quite simply by passing the whole range of colors coming from one prism through another prism, placed upside-down in relation to the first. The colors closed together, united, and came out as a shaft of pure white light!

Newton decided to call the range of colors that

make up white light the spectrum. Usually we say that there are six colors in the spectrum, but Newton, who was especially good at distinguishing colors, saw a seventh, indigo, between the violet and the blue.

Now that he had made these fundamental discoveries, Newton decided that the color trouble with lenses could never be cured, because white light would always split into colors when focused. We now know that he was wrong, because different kinds of glass bend light by different amounts, and a careful combination of glasses will yield a color-corrected lens.

However, Newton did not know this and so he resolved to sidestep the whole problem.

Different colors are bent through glass at different angles, but they are all reflected at the same angle. So he resolved to make a telescope that magnified by means of a mirror instead of a lens.

The idea of using a curved mirror to magnify in a telescope had already been suggested by James Gregory. Now, Newton decided that Gregory's idea was the only way to avoid the color trouble. He promised himself that he would try it out as soon as he got back to Cambridge.

Newton was back in his rooms in Trinity College, Cambridge, toward the end of March the following year. Having bought the necessary equipment, he set about making his telescope.

For the mirror he had to use polished metal, because at that time people had not discovered how to make glass mirrors by depositing silver on the glass. The metal was of an alloy he invented specifically for this purpose, composed of copper and tin together with a little arsenic.

He bought a crucible and melted the metals in it, keeping as far away from his work as he could because it created poisonous fumes. Then he cast and polished the metal until he had an excellent mirror.

The tube of the telescope, which he also made, was about six inches long and one inch across. It was mounted on a ball fitted into a socket so that the tube could easily be swiveled in any direction. The mirror rested at the closed bottom end of the tube and reflected the light back to a point near the open mouth. There the light was deflected sideways by a little mirror, and enlarged by a lens eyepiece set in the side of the telescope tube. Thus Newton still had one lens in his telescope, but it was small and did not give the trouble that a large lens would.

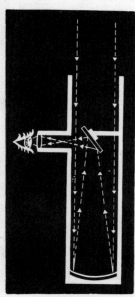

How a Newtonian reflector works. Light rays are gathered by the curved mirror at the bottom of the tube and reflected onto a mirror near the mouth. Then they are reflected again and focused (where the light rays cross). Finally they are magnified by the lense eyepiece. Different eyepieces give different magnifications.

He tested his telescope and was delighted to find that it worked beautifully. Although it was hardly larger than a toy, a friend saw the moons of Jupiter perfectly through it.

"My little telescope works better than an ordinary lens telescope four feet long," Newton wrote proudly. He calculated that it magnified some 35 times.

Later he made a larger reflecting telescope, which he gave to the Royal Society, a body of learned men which had recently been formed in London. It is still

treasured by the Society. However, Newton never made any systematic observations of the heavens.

When his work became known, other men seized eagerly on it and developed his ideas. By the time that color-corrected lenses had been devised, other advantages for mirrors were known, so that today the biggest light-gathering telescopes in the world are all reflectors.

But what of Newton's greatest discovery: the effects of gravity? Having forged the mathematical tools that he needed, he eventually worked through his theory in detail. Urged on by an English astronomer named Edmond Halley, he was able to show that he could account exactly for all the known movements in the Solar System. (Using his work, Halley correctly prophesied that a comet seen in 1682 would reappear in 1758.)

However, convincing as this feat was, Newton did not feel sure that gravity would also explain the mechanism of the universe beyond the Solar System. The man who was to probe far into the universe for the first time was William Herschel, using reflecting telescopes better than any the world had known.

HERSCHEL

On the night of March 1, 1774, William Herschel had just finished making his first reflecting telescope. It was 5½ feet long and of the Newtonian type.

Staggering under its weight, he and his brother Alexander proudly carried the instrument out into the garden. Their sister Caroline followed.

"Right here will do," said William, and the heavy telescope was put down on its stand.

Herschel was a successful music teacher and orchestra conductor in the fashionable city of Bath, in the west of England. His brother played the 'cello in the Bath Orchestra, and his sister was studying to be a singer. However, a year earlier, William had suddenly developed a passion for astronomy. Beginning by poring over books until he fell asleep buried under them, he went on to look at the skies himself.

To start with, he had rented telescopes; but none were good enough for him, so he had decided to build his own. Stumblingly, with nothing but a half-understood textbook on optics to guide him, he had designed his first reflecting telescope. Then, in moments snatched from his music, he had taken on the tedious chore of grinding and polishing it by hand. His brother Alexander had learned how to use a lens grinding machine and had set one up in a bedroom, where he made the eyepiece. A downstairs room was given up to a cabinet maker who produced the necessary tube and stand.

Now William was going to see the results of all this work. Eagerly he tilted the telescope toward the sky, and, with cries of delight, identified one object after another.

"Lina," he called to his sister, "I can see the rings of Saturn! How beautiful they are!"

He swung the telescope toward the constellation of Orion.

"There is a hazy white spot in the sword belt," he announced, puzzled. "Whatever it is, it does not look like a star."

Caroline looked through the telescope. She was just able to see because she was very short and the eyepiece was at the upper end of the tube. Meanwhile, William made notes about what he had seen. This was the beginning of his astronomical journal. (Later he was to know that the hazy white spot was a vast cloud of gas.)

The $5\frac{1}{2}$-foot telescope was a good beginning, but it did not satisfy Herschel for long. He yearned to look farther and farther into the heavens. A grand and audacious plan began to take shape in his mind. He wanted to understand the construction of the heavens.

To further his goal, he began work on a 7-foot reflector, with a correspondingly larger mirror.

"This will gather more light and reveal stars too faint to be seen with a smaller mirror," he reasoned. "And the fainter the stars I can see, the farther I shall be looking into space!"

He assumed that stars were, on an average, of the same real brightness; so that if a star appeared faint that meant it was a long, long ways away. This assumption was not entirely correct, but he was right when he believed that the more light he gathered, the farther he saw. Later he was able to determine that this worked on a simple proportion.

"If I double the diameter of a mirror, I double the distance I can see," he wrote.

The 7-foot telescope was still not enough for him. Intent upon increasing the power of his instruments, he followed it with a 10-foot, which had a mirror nearly 9 inches across instead of about $6\frac{1}{2}$ inches. Then he went still further and made a giant instrument 20 feet long, with a mirror 1 foot across. This was easily the most powerful telescope in the civilized world; and Herschel had made it unaided in his spare time. Also, since his knowledge of optics was still not too good, he made literally dozens of mirrors, trying them all out until he found the best ones.

By 1779 Herschel had amassed the best collection of telescopes in the world. Each was suitable for certain kinds of observing. Now he embarked on his immensely ambitious project of systematically cataloging the heavens. He began by reviewing the heavens as a whole.

For his first review he used a 7-foot Newtonian reflector which magnified 222 times. He noted the position of every star from the brightest down to fainter ones of the 4th magnitude. (A fairly bright star is of the 1st magnitude; the faintest visible with the naked eye are of the 6th.)

Besides doing this, he was completing a still better 7-foot instrument; and in August, 1779, he began a second review of the heavens with this. It had a mirror just over 6 inches across and magnified 227 times.

Because he had now rather foolishly moved to a house without a garden, he set up this telescope in the road outside. One night toward the end of December he was looking at the Moon, because he had also decided to measure the heights of the lunar mountains. A passer-by stopped and watched him curiously, but Herschel, who was not at all self-conscious, went on observing.

"Would you permit me to look through your telescope, sir?" asked the stranger eventually. He was elegantly dressed, with freshly curled wig and immaculate lace ruffles.

"Certainly," said Herschel with his usual generosity, and he stood aside at once.

The stranger peered and gave a gasp of surprise. He had looked at the Moon through telescopes before, but this instrument was better than any he had ever used.

"A marvelous view, sir," he said as he stepped back. Then he bowed courteously. "Thank you, and goodnight."

The next morning the mysterious stranger called at Herschel's house, No. 5 Rivers Street. The usual pandemonium of simultaneous music teaching and telescope making was going on.

"I am Dr. William Watson," he told Herschel. "I am a Fellow of the Royal Society and a member of the Bath Literary and Philosophical Society. After looking through your telescope last night, I realize that you are deeply interested in astronomy. I hope you will join our Bath Society."

Herschel was pleased, for evidently Dr. Watson was not only learned but prepared to take him seriously. Until then the people of Bath had thought of Herschel only as a musician with an eccentric taste for star-gazing.

Herschel joined the Literary and Philosophical Society and within a few days began to bombard them with accounts of his work. Between January, 1780, and March, 1781, he sent them 31 papers.

And then, on March 13th of that year, he saw something that was to make him known as an astronomer not only in Bath but throughout the world.

Using his best 7-foot reflector, he was busy with his second review of the heavens. This was a much more ambitious one than his first: he was now cataloging every star down to the 8th magnitude, as well as noting all double stars—that is, stars that seemed to appear in pairs. From his observations of the movements of these paired stars, he was later able to prove that Newton's laws of gravity did, indeed, apply outside the Solar System. He had now moved to a house with a garden and he was observing from the lawn. His sister Caroline usually sat nearby, noting down his observations, but on the night of March 13th she was not there.

Methodically, Herschel swept his telescope across the sky, pausing, counting, and moving on. Between 10 and 11 o'clock he reached a sector of sky in the constellation Gemini. Near one of the stars in the constellation he noticed something he had not seen before. It did not look like an ordinary star.

"Curious," he muttered, and looked harder. To try to determine what it was, he selected higher-power eye-pieces and looked at it with these. One brought the magnification up to 460, and the other to 932. The object looked proportionately bigger. This meant that it was fairly close; it was not a distant star which, because of certain optical effects, would not be magnified in proportion.

"Probably it is a comet," he decided.

To check on whether it was moving or not, he measured its distance from a neighboring star with a home-made micrometer and then, toward dawn, measured the distance again. It had changed.

"The object is definitely moving," he noted. "It must be a comet."

He was not very interested. What was one comet more or less, compared with the structure of the universe? Still, he dutifully wrote an account of what he had seen and sent off two copies, one to an astronomer at Oxford Observatory and the other to Dr. Watson. The doctor was intrigued and quickly passed the news on to the Astronomer Royal.

Dr. Nevil Maskelyne, the Astronomer Royal, was at Greenwich Observatory. He started hunting for the new comet as soon as possible and found it on April 3. Immediately, he was convinced that there was something strange about it.

"If it is a comet, it is very different from any that I have read about or seen," he wrote excitedly to Dr. Watson. "It is either a new sort of comet or a new planet."

A new planet! The idea was breathtaking. Throughout recorded history men had known of five planets, and five only.

Maskelyne pursued the idea. "It is as likely to be a regular planet moving in a nearly circular orbit round the Sun as a comet moving in a very elongated ellipse," he wrote Herschel on April 23. "I still have not seen any tail to it."

This made it less likely to be a comet, for all comets have tails as they near the Sun.

Meanwhile Herschel, who wanted to return to the depths of space, had been noting the position and size of the object each night. On April 26th the Royal Society received his description of the new comet, as he still believed it to be. Then he abandoned the matter to other astronomers.

They took up the problem eagerly. Everything depended on the shape of the orbit, as Maskelyne had pointed out. Was it a near-circle or an elongated ellipse?

Observations were collected, and in a few months the calculations could be made. Two mathematicians, Anders Johann Lexell of the St. Petersburg observatory in Russia, who happened to be in London, and Laplace, in France, figured the answer at the same time. The object was a planet circling the Sun beyond Saturn, and taking 84 years for a complete circuit. It was later christened Uranus.

For his part in this discovery, Herschel was awarded the Copley Medal, which is the highest honor the Royal Society can bestow; and on December 6, 1781, he was unanimously elected a Fellow of the Society. This meant that he was recognized as a scientist of the first rank.

Thanks to recommendations by the Astronomer Royal and others, King George III now granted Herschel an annual income. The only condition was that he should let the Royal Family peer through his telescopes from time to time.

This was just what Herschel needed. He could quit music teaching and throw himself full-time into astronomy. In 1782 he moved to Datchet, conveniently near the Royal household at Windsor. Aided by the indefatigable Caroline, he started on a still more ambitious program of work. (His brother Alexander was left in Bath to go on making his living as a musician.)

Now Herschel also became a professional telescope maker. His instruments were generally regarded as the finest in the world. After looking through Herschel's best 7-foot reflector, the Astronomer Royal had little use for his own 6-foot instrument.

"I doubt that it even deserves a new stand," he commented ruefully. Soon he ordered two of Herschel's 7-foot reflectors.

Other orders came pouring in. The King alone bought five 10-foot reflectors. Eventually Herschel found himself supplying leading astronomers all over Europe, to say nothing of various kings and princes. And somehow the incredible labor of making all these instruments was fitted in during the day while at night he went on with his observing.

A few months after the move to Datchet, Herschel received a letter from a friend named Alexander Aubert, who was an amateur astronomer. With the letter came a list noting the positions of strange, cloudy objects in the sky that had been sighted by a famous French comet hunter, Charles Messier.

"This sounds intriguing, Lina," commented Herschel. "Messier has cataloged these cloudy objects because they look like comets and he does not want to keep mixing them up. I must have a look at them!"

He started to examine all 103 of the listed objects. At first he used his old 20-foot reflector, but then he transferred to his latest, most powerful model with a mirror 1½ feet across.

To hold the telescope, Herschel had had a big wooden structure erected in the garden. There was a system of ropes and pulleys for adjusting the direction and angle of the tube. He observed the sky from a movable gallery that could be raised to as much as 15 feet above the ground. Caroline sat below to note the observations he called out, a star atlas open before her.

With this excellent telescope, Herschel soon arrived at a conclusion that Messier had never dreamed of. He seperated out distinct individual stars in some of these distant cloudy nebulae, and saw that the stars were tightly grouped in clumps of clusters. Actually the clusters where he could see stars were much nearer than most of the nebulae. But he now guessed that all the cloudy objects were really vast groups of stars.

Where did these great systems of stars lie? With an inspired bound of imagination, Herschel proposed that they could be much farther away than ordinary stars, and that our Sun was in a similar system, visible, perhaps, to us as the Milky Way.

"Maybe there are many of these great systems, all separate from each other," he ventured. "Maybe they are whole separate universes—island universes!"

When they heard of this idea, his contemporaries

laughed. This was pure imagination, not hard-headed observation. They could not believe in systems of stars beyond the ordinary stars they were used to.

But Herschel was not deterred. He started to catalog these mysterious groups of cloudy nebulae, convinced that they all would reveal themselves as great star systems if he could only see them with a powerful enough telescope.

"I have discovered 1,500 whole star systems, some of which may well exceed our own Milky Way in grandeur," he wrote later.

Then he really let himself go and imagined that these far-away island universes might be peopled with inhabitants scrutinizing our own star system.

"To them, our system must assume different guises, depending on how far away they are," he brooded. "To some, it will be a small, nebulous patch; to others, an extended streak of milky light, or a very compressed cluster of small stars; and to still others an immense collection of large scattered stars."

Now he set himself the task of trying to decipher the shape of our own star system, assuming that we saw it as the Milky Way. He knew that this runs in a band across the northern sky and the southern sky as well. Eventually he pictured it as a great layer of stars that stretched out in a round, flat disk. Being in the middle of this disk, he argued, we would see it as a band going around us.

But if this were true, how could he gauge the diameter and thickness of the disk? He decided to assume that all the stars in it were, on an average, evenly spaced out—just as, on an average, everyone in a crowd has the same distance between himself and his neighbors.

"If this is so, the areas that seem to be crowded will really be those where I am looking at a deep layer of stars," he reasoned. "Similarly, an area with a few stars will be a shallow layer."

To use this ingenious way of taking depth soundings, he had to count stars in selected areas. It was incredibly painstaking work. Night after night he mounted to the gallery and counted, while the faithful Caroline sat below and noted everything that he found. In some parts of the sky, on each side of the Milky Way, he might find only one star in view at a time. In the Milky Way itself, he might find as many as 500 at once.

He spent all his observing time on this job from the beginning of 1784 until early in the next year. The general pattern became clear fairly soon, but he made 683 separate soundings, or star counts, before he was satisfied.

"The Milky Way is undoubtedly a most extensive disk of stars," he announced at last. "Its diameter is about four times greater than its central thickness. And our Sun is definitely one of the stars belonging to it."

We now know that all the true stars we see with the unaided eye belong to the Milky Way, our galaxy, and that the band of dense stars is merely the area that looks most concentrated to us, because of our position in the galaxy. And the whole is far bigger than Herschel dreamed. Nevertheless, Herschel had made a marvelous attempt to gauge the depths of the Milky Way. His limitations were not limitations of personal vision, but of means for measuring distances; he had no way of measuring the distance away of even one star.

And what of his great vision of other galaxies, or island universes, out in the deeps of space? His contemporaries could not follow him so far, nor could many astronomers later. It was only after some 150 years that Edwin Hubble, an American astronomer, finally proved Herschel right.

Long before then, however, the first step had been taken in making an exact measure of our own galaxy. The man to take this step was a German named Friedrich Wilhelm Bessel.

BESSEL

ONE COLD DAY in the fall of 1829, a horse-drawn wagon creaked heavily through the cobbled streets of Königsberg, in East Prussia. It was bringing a new telescope to the observatory above the town. As it began laboring up the hill, Friedrich Wilhelm Bessel, the director of the observatory, watched it impatiently.

"At last, here is my Fraunhofer!" he exclaimed. "Now I shall find out if they are as good as they are said to be."

Joseph Fraunhofer was an Austrian telescope maker who had set out to design refracting telescopes that would work even better than Herschel's reflectors. By using special color-corrected lenses, he had succeeded. The object glass at the front of a Fraunhofer telescope gathered as much light as a mirror double the size, be-

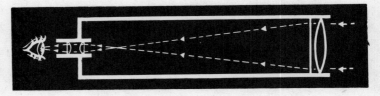

How a modern refracting telescope works. Light is gathered by a color-free combination of two lenses made of different kinds of glass. Then the light is focused (where the rays cross) and magnified by the eyepiece. Different eyepieces give different magnifications.

cause the metal mirrors then used were inefficient. Soon professional astronomers everywhere were clamoring for a Fraunhofer refractor.

Among them was Bessel. A refractor was especially suitable for making careful measurements, and a Fraunhofer refractor could yield more accurate results than any other. Every astronomer wants accurate instruments, but Bessel prized accuracy above everything. He had long ago stopped trusting any instruments.

"Every telescope is made twice," he used to say, "first in the workshop and then by the astronomer."

With endless patience, he always checked the performance of his instruments and located any inaccuracies, however small.

The early equipment in his observatory had included a meridian circle by a British manufacturer, Cary. Used for measuring the apparent distance between two stars, this telescope turned on an axis that had to be precisely at right angles to its lenses. Bessel found that it was not. However, he worked out a way of compensating for this flaw.

He ferreted out other sources of error. The atmosphere, like a prism, bends the light reaching us from the stars. But it does not always bend the light by the same amount: the bending varies with the temperature and pressure of the air. Bessel improved on earlier formulas devised to allow for these changes. Embodied in tables, his correcting figures were eagerly adopted by astronomers everywhere.

Bessel was dissatisfied with the Earth, too: as a platform from which to observe the stars, it is hopelessly unsteady. The axis on which it spins shifts in direction and wobbles slightly. However, he managed to frame corrections for these movements.

And now at last he had a telescope designed by an equally exact man. It was soon set up on its heavy oak frame in a tower that had been specially built to house it. The polished wooden tube, some 10 feet long and covered with mahogany, shone like burnished copper. Bessel touched it gingerly and found to his amazement that he could swing the heavy instrument anywhere at the touch of a finger because of built-in counterweights. Better still, there was a motor that, geared to a clock, would keep the instrument automatically trained on a star for hours, despite the rotation of the Earth.

"This is good, very good!" murmured Bessel.

What of the object glass? Used for gathering light, it was $6\frac{1}{4}$ inches wide and made of a color-correcting combination of glasses. Bessel peered at it with his large, acute eyes—eyes that, when he was a boy of 13, had shown him a double star where astronomers had noted only one. Then he drew a satisfied breath: the lens was of flawless glass, and was the best he had ever seen.

He thought of the lens mounting. In warm weather

the lens would expand a trifle. He pounced on it suspiciously—and discovered that the indefatigable Fraunhofer had made a special split elastic frame to accommodate the lens as it expanded.

"Splendid!" cried Bessel. Fraunhofer was obviously a man after his own heart.

Just the same, he checked out the whole instrument. When he was finished, he was delighted. Fraunhofer had foreseen everything—at least, everything except one minute detail. The scale of the device used for gauging distances in the field of view would change fractionally in length with alterations in the air temperature. But Bessel knew he could measure the changes and make the necessary corrections.

He was happy; he had one of the finest telescopes in the world. The closest rival was another Fraunhofer, built for F. G. W. Struve at the Dorpat Observatory in Russia. But that was not so good for making precise measurements.

"With this telescope," said Bessel, "I can try to find out how far away a star is!"

Bessel knew that since the time of Newton, men had tried to do this and failed. The reason was the fantastically small measurements involved.

The only way that it seemed possible to find the distance of a star was to measure its annual parallax. This is the apparent shift of its position through the year when compared to more distant; seemingly fixed stars visible in the same area of the sky. The effect is due to the varying angle at which an observer on Earth views the stars during the Earth's annual trip round the Sun. The same sort of effect occurs if one holds up a finger and looks at it first with one eye, then the other. The finger appears to shift sideways in comparison with objects behind.

Since the Earth's orbit is 180 million miles across, every six months we are 180 million miles away from the place we were six months before, and we are seeing any given star from a position that much different. Using this fact, the six-monthly shift of a star against near stars in the background can, by simple geometry, reveal its distance from us. The bigger the shift appears to be, the nearer the star must be. However, even the nearest star is so far away that we cannot discern this shift with the naked eye.

In Newton's time, astronomers turned their crude telescopes to the stars, hoping that these would reveal shifts due to parallax. At first they believed that they had succeeded, but later James Bradley, the third Astronomer Royal, proved that all they were measuring was observational error.

By refining his technique, allowing for one sort of error after another, Bradley managed to achieve an accuracy of 1 second of arc. This was over two hundred times better than Tycho Brahe's usual standard, but it still was not good enough to reveal any parallax.

After that astronomers quit trying for a while. Struve had even proved that with existing instruments it was impossible to measure the minute changes involved. However, that was before he got his Fraunhofer.

Now that Bessel, too, was armed with a Fraunhofer, he felt ready to try making the necessary measurements. Even so, he wanted to choose a star that would show the maximum parallax.

"The nearer a star is to us, the greater the parallax," he mused. "But how can I decide which is a nearby star?"

To determine this, he did a little detective work. For some time, astronomers had realized that the so-called "fixed" stars, fixed because their relationships to each other in the sky remain the same, are not fixed at all. Some of them can be seen to move steadily across the sky. Because they are so far away, the movement is minute, but it can be measured.

In 1792 an Italian monk, Guiseppe Piazzi, had pointed out that one star was moving particularly fast. Located in the constellation of Cygnus, the Swan, it was designated 61 Cygni. Astronomers nicknamed it the "flying star." Not that it moved fast enough to see with the naked eye; from the time of Kepler to the present day it has only traveled an amount equal to the apparent width of the Moon. Nevertheless Bessel decided that such visible speed and movement indicated 61 Cygni was nearby.

"Probably all the stars are really moving at much the same speed," he argued, "however, the nearer ones appear to be moving faster just because they are near."

It was a bold deduction, but it gave him a good reason for choosing this star. Also, 61 Cygni is near the Pole Star, and so it would remain above the horizon most of the year.

In 1834, after completing a program of other work, Bessel made his first attack on the problem. As reference points for judging the annual shift of the star, he chose two stars of the eleventh magnitude. However, he soon found that it was very difficult to observe these faint stars accurately.

"I shall have to use brighter reference stars," he decided.

But now other interests kept claiming his time. Hal-

ley's comet reappeared in 1835, and Bessel, entranced, watched it on every clear night. Then he took on the complicated chore of calculating the length of one degree on the Earth's surface, or 1/360 of its circumference.

It was not until August, 1837, that he was able to concentrate on his parallax measurements. For his new reference stars he selected two whose brilliance lay between the ninth and tenth magnitudes. One was in the line of travel of 61 Cygni, and the other was at right angles to this line.

Training his Fraunhofer on each of these stars in turn, and keeping 61 Cygni in view at the same time, he read off the angular distances between them and 61 Cygni. The screws of the measuring device were so finely adjusted that he could measure to an accuracy of one twentieth of a second of arc—which is less than the width of a pinhead viewed from a distance of two miles.

"The star in the line of travel is 11 minutes 46 seconds away," he noted. "The other is 7 minutes 42 seconds away."

After that, every night when the sky was clear, he said goodnight to his wife and three children and walked through the sleeping town to the observatory. There he looked again at his stars and carefully recorded the changes in position he saw. On ordinary nights he repeated each measurement sixteen times, and when the air was particularly steady he took even more.

By day, Bessel shut himself away in his study and worked over his figures, whittling away the observational errors he knew he had to allow for. He also had to correct for the actual movement of the "flying star," and to do this he enlisted the help of a former assistant named Friedrich Argelander. Working at Bonn Observatory, Argelander used past observations of the star made in 1755 and 1830 to work out its rate of travel.

Bessel knew that the parallax effect would make the star appear to travel in a tiny ellipse during the year. As he pored over his figures each day, sifting them and correcting them, he watched eagerly for any sign of this tell-tale ellipse. In a month or so he was sure he noticed it.

To the scientific world, however, he said nothing. He needed a full year's results first.

Fall came, and Bessel went up to the unheated observatory tower in his topcoat. The first snow of winter settled on Königsberg, and then the ponds froze over. Bessel, who was now 54 years old, doggedly continued with his observations. Every night he huddled in the tower, making delicate adjustments with numbed fingers, trying not to let his breath fog the eyepiece.

By the time six months had passed, he knew that he had succeeded. The parallactic shift was plainly revealed in his figures. But he went right on observing, grimly resolved to get a full year's data.

At last, by the end of the summer of 1838, he had all the observations and calculations he needed. To make quite sure, he checked them all through for possible errors and then, in December, he published them.

"The annual parallax of 61 Cygni is 0.3136 second of arc," he announced proudly. "This means that it is 657,700 times farther away than the Sun. Light takes 10.3 years to travel from it to us."

He wrote his results down matter-of-factly, but the figures were staggering. Astronomers had expected immense distances, but even so they were appalled at the vastness of the universe. Since light travels at 186,000 miles a second, the 10.3 years represented 60 trillion miles. And this was to one of the nearest stars!

We now know that even Bessel was not perfectly accurate. The modern parallax value for 61 Cygni is just about 0.30 second of arc, which represents a distance from us of 66 trillion miles. However, his figures were the best available for a long while.

Soon after he had announced his result, two other astronomers came up with figures for other stars. Thomas Henderson, Astronomer Royal for Scotland, had been making measurements on Alpha Centauri, and F. G. W. Struve at Dorpat had used his Fraunhofer to get a value for Vega. However, both results were later found to be too big.

With these measurements, men were beginning to understand the isolation of the stars. The nearest star to our own Sun is Alpha Centauri, which is 4.3 light years away. A modern space craft going 25,000 miles an hour could travel the distance to the Moon—nearly 240,000 miles—in ten hours and in 20 years could reach the edge of the Solar System. However, it would need to keep going at the same rate for about 120,000 years to reach Alpha Centauri.

Nowadays astronomers use photographs taken at different times to reveal parallax shifts. Averaging the results of many photographs, they can measure parallax changes with an accuracy of 1/200 of a second of arc. The distances of about 5,000 stars have been determined in this way. Most stars, however, are so far from us that this method is of no use.

Bessel, having disposed of 61 Cygni, soon turned to

another problem. Astronomers everywhere were beginning to examine the strange behavior of Uranus, the planet discovered by William Herschel. An orbit had been calculated for this planet, and for a while men had believed that it was following the plotted orbit exactly. Then, in 1825, astronomers noticed that Uranus was running ahead of its expected positions. One or two astronomers considered working out the orbit again.

But before they could do so, Uranus began slowing down. By 1830, it was back on the track prophesied for it. It seemed that the first calculations were not so bad after all. But Uranus went on slowing down, and in another two years it was nearly half a minute of arc behind. This was an enormous discrepancy.

Hoping to solve the mystery, Bessel took on a promising young English astronomer named Flemming as an assistant. Bessel had decided that the first step toward finding an answer was checking the accuracy of all the existing observations of Uranus, and he needed help in this painstaking work.

By 1840 Bessel was sure of his results.

"The existing differences, which in some cases exceed a whole minute of arc, are not due to faulty observations," he told an audience at Königsberg.

This meant that Uranus was definitely running behind the schedule calculated for it. But why?

"I believe," said ·Bessel, "that the cause is an unknown planet whose pull is affecting Uranus!"

Soon after making this daring prophecy, Bessel became ill and could not go on with the work. However, two young men, one in France and one in England, took up the problem.

ADAMS & LEVERRIER

TOWARD the end of June, 1841, a quiet, shy undergraduate named John Couch Adams entered Johnson's bookstore in Cambridge, England. He often browsed in this store, for he lived nearby.

Glancing along the shelves, he noticed a dusty old astronomical report written ten years earlier. It dealt with the movements of Uranus and its author was George Biddell Airy, who had since become the Astronomer Royal. Curious, Adams took it down and began to look through it.

"The movements of the planets can usually be prophesied from Newton's law of gravity," wrote Airy. "However, we cannot accurately prophesy the movements of Uranus."

Adams raised his eyebrows in astonishment. The

movements of the other planets were so well-known that the Solar System seemed like a piece of perfect clockwork.

"Some astronomers believe that this outermost planet is being affected by the pull of still another, unknown planet beyond it," Airy continued. "Other astronomers, including myself, believe our calculations are wrong because Newton's law does not apply so far from the Sun."

Adams put the report down indignantly.

"Newton's law has been found correct so far," he told himself. "Why assume it is wrong now, just because we are baffled by Uranus?"

He felt sure that Airy was wrong to doubt Newton's law. This meant that there must be an undiscovered eighth planet in the sky somewhere. But where?

As the young undergraduate left the bookstore, he brooded over the problem. He crossed Trinity Street and walked past the mellow brick buildings to the college rooms in which he lived. As he walked, a great ambition took hold of him.

"I will calculate whether the movements of Uranus can be explained by an eighth planet," he decided. "Then, if they can, I will try to figure its orbit. This will probably lead to its discovery!"

It was two years before he could begin this complicated mathematical research. First came the studies for his bachelor's degree, which he received at the beginning of 1843. Then there were various teaching duties. Meanwhile, he told James Challis, the professor of astronomy at Cambridge, about his plan. Challis was eager to help.

"Here are some books you may need," he said, taking a selection from the crowded shelves in his study. "Let me know if I can help in any other way."

At last a long summer vacation began, and Adams had time to start work on his calculations. Taking a trunkful of books with him, he set off by stagecoach for his family's farm in Lidcot, Cornwall. There he would have the peace and quiet that he needed.

All through that vacation John Adams grappled with his research. He went out for walks with his brother George but hardly noticed anything around him. His mind was full of equations and the data accumulated from hundreds of observations of Uranus. He sat up late each evening at a table in the little parlor, copying out columns of figures, adding and subtracting, giving the results to George to check, until his brother begged him to go to bed.

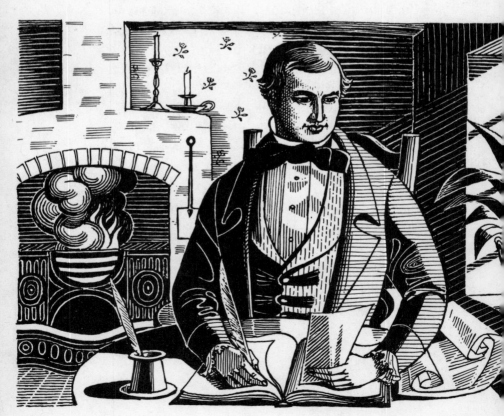

"In a minute," John Adams would mutter, and go on working for hours longer. All he wanted was to get his calculations done.

By the time he returned to Cambridge in October, he had a rough answer. He hurried to tell Challis of his result.

"I am sure that another planet is orbiting beyond Uranus!" he announced excitedly. "But I must have more data before I can map the orbit precisely."

Adams knew that Airy, the Astronomer Royal, was then extracting important data from observations made during the eight years between 1818 and 1826.

"Can you help me get those figures?" he asked Challis.

The professor was glad to aid his student. He wrote off to the Astronomer Royal at Greenwich Observatory and got the essential figures very soon.

However, Adams did not get to work on these for quite a while. He had university duties that took up most of his time. Instead of trying to discover a new planet, he had to concentrate on official chores and teaching commitments. Fortunately he was in no hurry. The problem was fascinating, but not, he felt, urgent.

In the spring of 1844, he finally took time out from his college duties to finish framing the formulas he needed; but he still had to see how the actual observations fit in with these. He did not finish his work until September. But then he had the size of the unknown planet and its exact orbit.

Proudly, he showed Challis the results. The professor examined them eagerly. It was a marvelous piece of mathematical analysis: every detail about the planet was prophesied.

"You must send these to the Astronomer Royal at once!" urged Challis.

"I can take them to him," replied Adams. "I am just about to go home to Cornwall and can deliver them on the way."

Challis agreed that this was a good idea and wrote a letter of introduction for the young mathematician to present to the Astronomer Royal. But when Adams arrived at Greenwich, he learned that Airy was attending a conference in Paris. Disappointed, he left the letter of introduction and went on to Cornwall.

A week later, Airy returned and found the letter. He wrote immediately to Challis.

"I am much interested in Mr. Adams' investigations," he said. "I should be delighted to hear of them by letter from him."

However, Adams still wanted to deliver his results personally. Returning from Cornwall near the end of October, he tried again. He called in the morning at the imposing house occupied by the Astronomer Royal and found only the butler. He left his card, to show that he had called, and also left the precious results, promising to call again in the afternoon.

When he came back around 4 o'clock, he was sure that at last he would see the great astronomer and be able to explain his work. To his amazement, the butler turned him away.

"The Astronomer Royal is eating and cannot be disturbed," he said haughtily.

In actual fact, the butler wanted to protect his master from being disturbed at mealtime. He never told him of Adams' visit. But Adams, who did not know this, was much upset.

"The Astronomer Royal regards his meal as more important than my new planet," he thought. "He cannot even be bothered to see me."

Adams returned to Cambridge, but he had left the crucial data behind. In this he prophesied that the unknown planet would be in an orbit lying some 2.8 billion miles from the Sun—or roughly twice as far as Uranus. Its weight would be a little more than that of Uranus, and about 17 times that of the Earth. He also stated just where it would have been in the sky three weeks earlier.

This prediction was an extraordinary mathematical feat. However, the Astronomer Royal was not enthusiastic about it; if correct, it would prove him wrong. He still believed that the discrepancies in the movements of Uranus were only apparent, and that Newton's law of gravity did not hold good so far from the Sun.

"Has some young nobody of 26 really solved a mystery that has baffled leading astronomers for years?" he asked himself suspiciously.

It was too much for Airy to swallow. He could easily have tested the prophecy by turning the Greenwich telescope to the sky where Adams indicated. Instead, he stalled by writing a non-committal letter to Adams, asking for further, but quite unnecessary, information.

The poor young mathematician was baffled. He had eagerly given the result of all his painstaking work to the official leader of British astronomy. Now he felt utterly discouraged and gave up trying to persuade Airy of the worth of his work.

"I have done all I can," he said.

Meanwhile a brilliant young astronomer in Paris

had begun working on the same problem. His name was Urbain Jean Joseph Leverrier, and he was some eight years older than Adams. He delighted in long, complicated mathematical analysis of the kind needed. Now, spurred on by François Arago, the leading French astronomer, he determined to explain the movements of Uranus. He had no idea that someone else across the English Channel had been attempting the same thing.

He started work in June, 1845—just two months before Adams completed his calculations. Leverrier threw himself into the task, and by November he had already made his preliminary analysis of the problem. He worked to unheard-of accuracy, noting every discrepancy down to as little as one-twentieth of a second of arc.

"The cause of the discrepancies is an unknown planet beyond Uranus," he told the French Academy of Sciences.

But where was this planet and how big was it? Like Adams, Leverrier saw that if he could calculate the answers to these questions, astronomers should be able to pick out the planet with their telescopes.

Day after day, he went to his study in the Ecole Polytechnique and grappled with thousands of figures. The clatter of horses' hooves and the shouts of street vendors came up from below, but he hardly heard them. Sifting figures and fitting them to formulas he devised, he gradually whittled down the possibilities. By early summer, in 1846, he was able to state where the planet should be at the beginning of the next year. Although he did not know it, the position was only one degree of arc different from that prophesied by Adams.

"Let us hope," wrote Leverrier, "that we will succeed in sighting the planet whose position I have given."

His results reached George Airy toward the end of June. Despite himself, the Astronomer Royal was impressed.

"Adams and Leverrier have independently gotten the same result," he thought. "Maybe there is something in this idea after all."

And so, eight months after getting the data from Adams, the Astronomer Royal began to take action. On July 9, he wrote to Challis asking him to use his great 12-inch refractor to search for the planet. At that time the Cambridge telescope was the largest in Britain.

"I suggest that you search three times over a band of sky 30 degrees long and 10 degrees wide, mapping all the brighter stars," he wrote. "In this way you should eventually find the planet if it is there."

There were some 3,000 stars to map. The method of search was hopelessly inefficient—somewhat like trying to find a friend in a crowded grandstand by noting the person in every seat. However, Challis gallantly agreed to try it.

Meanwhile, Leverrier came up with an incredibly exact prophecy of the planet's position and sent it to the French Academy of Sciences at the end of August.

"The planet is now very well placed for observation," he added excitedly. "Its disk should appear near its maximum, about 3.3 seconds of arc in width."

The French astronomers, however, did nothing. Like Airy, they doubted that a young man using only pencil and paper could achieve so much. Not one of them even suggested turning his telescope to the place Leverrier had computed.

"If only I had my own telescope!" mourned Leverrier. He was growing desperate.

And then he remembered Johann Gottfried Galle, a young astronomer at the Berlin Observatory, who had written to him earlier about another matter.

On September 18, 1846, he wrote to Galle begging him to search for the planet. With the letter went all the data describing the orbit.

Galle seized upon the idea immediately.

"May I search for this planet?" he asked Johann Franz Encke, the elderly director of the observatory.

"It sounds like a waste of time to me," muttered Encke testily.

Galle pleaded and argued for some precious telescope time. At last the director gave way. That night, September 23rd, the dome of the observatory slid open and the 9-inch Fraunhofer refractor turned toward the area indicated by Leverrier. Galle sat at the controls, and a student named Heinrich Louis d'Arrest was at a desk with a star atlas.

Galle trained the telescope exactly on the spot predicted for the planet for that night by Leverrier.

"Right ascension 22 hours 46 minutes, and declination minus 13 degrees 24 minutes," he whispered.

Excitedly he peered at the tiny area of sky. There was nothing resembling a planet.

"We will have to search around the area," he told d'Arrest. "As I call out the position and appearance of each object, check to see if it is marked on the star map."

The first object was definitely a star. So was the second. So was the third. The fourth seemed to be of the eighth magnitude. Galle called out its position.

"Right ascension 22 hours 53 minutes 25.84 seconds."

Feverishly d'Arrest searched for it.

"That is not on the map!" he exclaimed at last.

The two young men stared at each other, their faces alight with excitement.

"The eighth planet," whispered Galle, hardly daring to believe it. "And less than a degree from where Leverrier prophesied!"

The next night he managed to measure its movement, thus confirming the fact that it was the unknown planet. Jubilantly, he dashed off a letter to the French astronomer.

"The planet whose position you have pointed out *actually exists*," he wrote.

Within a few days Leverrier had christened the new planet Neptune.

When Challis heard the news, he was still doggedly searching the sky, following Airy's advice. Now he checked his records and found, to his chagrin, that he had seen the planet twice without realizing it.

"After only four days of observing, the planet was in my grasp," he wrote mournfully to Airy.

He blamed himself for not spotting the planet, but British astronomers blamed Airy more. Soon they were angrily asking why he had not acted earlier, instead of letting the prize go to France.

"Adams had the orbit long before Leverrier," they said. "He should be regarded as the discover of Neptune."

When Leverrier heard this, he was much upset.

"If Mr. Adams had the result, why did he keep silent?" he wrote to Airy. "And why did you not mention his results if you knew of them?"

Arago also challenged the British claims. In a sarcastic speech before the French Academy of Sciences, he jeered at Airy and Challis for failing to act on Adams' calculations or even to publicize his theory.

"There is no mention of any publication of Mr. Adams' work," he cried. "Without publication, how can we believe any of these claims? Mr. Adams has no right to appear in the history of the discovery of the planet!"

The quarrel between the British and French astronomers went on for the better part of a year. And what started out as an astronomical quarrel soon became a national quarrel between the two countries. Meanwhile, the two men most concerned, Adams and Leverrier, took no part in it.

In June, 1847, the British Association for the Advancement of Science held its annual meeting. Sir John

Herschel, son of the great William and a distinguished astronomer himself, invited Leverrier and Adams to his home at Collingwood afterward. There they strolled together under the elms, obviously admiring each other and quite free of jealousy. They were to remain friends for the rest of their lives.

Adams and Leverrier proved that Newton's law of gravity could be used to deduce the existence of bodies far out in space. Their methods have since helped to make further discoveries.

By studying the behavior of Uranus and Neptune, Percival Lowell in Arizona decided that there must be still another planet to explain the irregularities in their movements. A search therefore started for a ninth planet in the Solar System. After many years, it was found when an assistant at the Lowell Observatory named Clyde W. Tombaugh identified it on February 18, 1930. It was named Pluto.

Similar methods have shown that other stars beside the sun have their own planets. By studying any deviation from what might be expected in the way a star moves, astronomers can deduce the presence of a planet, and its size. One of the latest to be discovered was announced by Peter van de Kamp, director of the Sproul Observatory in Pennsylvania, in April, 1963. Belonging to Barnard's Star, which is 6 light years away, it weighs about 500 times as much as the Earth.

However, this method only works with nearby stars whose movements can be studied closely. Millions of other stars probably have attendant planets, but astronomers do not expect now that they will ever detect them.

FRAUNHOFER & KIRCHOFF

THE LARGE ROOM was dark except for a narrow shaft of sunlight coming through a vertical slit in the window shutter. Twenty-four feet away, Joseph Fraunhofer adjusted a special flint-glass prism in front of the small telescope of a theodolite. The sunlight entered the prism, bent through it, and passed into the little telescope. By looking through this, Fraunhofer could see the spectrum of sunlight under high magnification.

Carefully he adjusted the eyepiece of the telescope until the spectrum came sharply into focus. He expected to see bands of color, just as Newton had. And that is what he did see—but he also saw hundreds of fine dark lines running down them!

Puzzled, he wiped the eyepiece and looked again. The lines were still there.

"Maybe there is some fault in the prism," he muttered.

Getting up, he exchanged the one prism for another. But when he came back and examined the spectrum again, he still saw the mysterious lines.

He finally decided that the lines were obviously part of the sunlight. But what were they? Did they appear in other kinds of light as well?

Fraunhofer wanted to find out because he felt that the more he knew about light the better would be the lenses he made. Already he was famous for the wonderful refracting telescopes he had designed, but he never stopped trying to make even better ones. The Austrian firm of Utzschneider and Reichenbach, for which he worked, had come to realize that young Fraunhofer was not only a technician, but a researcher. And because his research proved valuable to them, they let him experiment when he wished.

Next Fraunhofer examined the spectrum of candlelight. To his surprise, there were no dark lines; but there were two bright lines in the yellow part of the spectrum. What did this mean?

The young Austrian did not know, but at least he had discovered that not all kinds of light are the same. He set himself to describing the strange dark lines in sunlight. Some were darker than others and stood out like definite bars: there was one in the red, a strong one in the blue, two close together in the yellow . . .

"Two in the yellow!" he exclaimed, remembering the bright lines in the yellow of candlelight.

Going back to the spectrum of candlelight, he checked the exact position of the two bright lines. They were in exactly the same place as the dark lines in the yellow in the spectrum of sunlight.

Without knowing what this meant, Fraunhofer noted it down. Then he went on studying the spectrum of sunlight. He had decided to make a chart of all the dark lines he could see. There were eight particularly prominent lines, and he labeled these by letters, from *A* to *H*. The two lines close together in the yellow were allocated just one letter, *D*. Using a homemade micrometer, he measured just how far apart these lines were in the telescope and drew them carefully on his chart. Then he drew all the fainter lines in between. It was a long, hard job, but he kept at it day after day until he was red-eyed and weary. Eventually he had noted down a total of 574 separate lines, and there were many others too close together for him to count.

Fascinated by these mysterious spectral lines, Fraunhofer next decided to investigate light from the planets and the stars. He wanted to see if their light had the same lines as sunlight.

To do this work, he made a 4½-inch refracting telescope and mounted a prism in front of it. When it was finished, he took this special telescope up to his apartment and, as soon as it was dark, began by looking at Venus. No shutter and slit were needed this time; there was little enough light.

By peering hard, Fraunhofer could see the same dark spectral lines, although they were barely visible in the red and violet parts of the spectrum, which generally appear dimmest. Otherwise the spectrum appeared to be the same as the one he had seen with sunlight. This was what he had expected, because Venus and other planets shine by reflected sunlight and have no light of their own. To check further, however, he measured the positions of the main lines with a homemade micrometer. They were identical to those in the sunlight spectrum.

Now Fraunhofer turned to some stars. Selecting the brightest to start with, he looked at Sirius.

"Only three dark bands!" he exclaimed.

He gazed until his eyes watered, but still he could not see any more lines. This spectrum was quite different from the spectrum of sunlight.

"One band is in the green, and two are in the blue," he noted.

But what did the lines mean? The young Austrian realized that he had stumbled on some secret of the stars. These strange lines contained a message in code. He could not read the code, but for a while he went on hunting spectra. He found that Castor was like Sirius, but four other stars—Pollux, Capella, Betelgeux, and Procyon —resembled our own star, the Sun. In all these he saw the same two *D* lines that were in the sunlight's spectrum.

This was as far as he could go. In 1815, he announced his results to the Munich Academy. However, he had found no way of explaining them. The spectral codes remained unbroken.

The man who solved the codes was Gustav Robert Kirchoff, a precise and rather pedantic professor of physics at the University of Heidelberg in Germany.

He started by studying not dark lines but bright ones. Together with Robert Wilhelm Bunsen, professor of chemistry at the same university, he was investigating the fact that chemical elements give out light when heated. They used a special kind of gas burner invented by Bunsen to heat chemicals. When they put a chemical

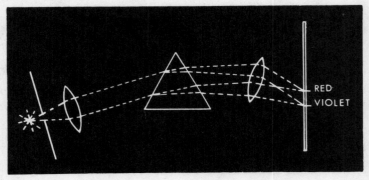

How a modern spectroscope works. Light comes through a narrow slit and is made into a parallel beam by a lens. Then the light is bent by a prism which separates the constituent colors. The colors are focused by another lens, giving a sharp spectrum. This spectrum can be viewed on a screen as shown or through a lense eyepiece which magnifies it.

into the flame of the burner, they found that each different chemical colored the flame with its own special color and this gave a way of identifying the chemical.

Looking at the flame through a spectroscope—which is an improved version of Fraunhofer's little theodolite telescope—the two men discovered that each special color created its own bright bands of light, located in just certain parts of the spectrum. Thus table salt gave off a bright yellow light, and in the spectroscope this showed up as two bright lines close together in the yellow region of the spectrum. These two lines were the same lines that Fraunhofer had labeled *D* lines. Table salt contains sodium, and the two bright *D* lines were the spectral code for sodium.

By heating chemicals containing other elements, they found the codes for these, too. A bright red line plus a bright orange one meant lithium. Barium was revealed by four bright lines of various colors. For iron there were over a thousand lines. It was soon clear that when a chemical element is heated to a point where it gives out light, the light it gives will appear in just certain parts of the spectrum and no other. Some elements sent out light at many parts, some sent out light at only a few. But all had a special pattern.

Once he had established these patterns, Kirchoff began to wonder about the dark spectral lines which Fraunhofer had found. These were the opposite: they meant that no light was being sent out at the parts of the spectrum where they occurred. Why was this?

To try to solve this problem, Kirchoff set up a new series of experiments. He began them one sunny morning in October, 1859. Going into his laboratory, the frock-coated and bearded professor set up his usual arrangement of bunsen burner and table salt to give the bright yellow spectrum of sodium. But this time, instead of just looking at the sodium, he arranged his Steinheil spectroscope so that he could examine sunlight from the window after it had passed through the sodium flame.

"I shall see all the dark lines in the sunlight except for the two D lines," he prophesied as he settled himself on a stool. "The D lines will be overlaid by the bright D lines from the sodium."

Eagerly he peered through the spectroscope to see if his guess was correct. Then he caught his breath: the dark D lines had not disappeared. On the contrary, they were sharper than ever!

"The sodium flame must have stopped sending out its bright lines," mused Kirchoff. "It must have done this because of the sunlight."

He could not imagine why this should have happened. Did the brightness of the sunlight have anything to do with it? To find out, he tried reducing the amount of sunlight reaching the sodium flame. As the sunlight was dimmed, he saw the dark spectral D lines grow fainter. And then, without warning, two bright D lines suddenly shone out again in his spectrum.

"When the sunlight is dim enough, the sodium flame sends out its yellow light again," noted Kirchoff. "But why did it ever stop?"

To try to find out, he decided to send pure white light, free of dark lines, through the flame. The other dark lines in sunlight made it difficult for him to see exactly what was happening to the sodium spectrum.

To get pure white light he used a special Drummond lamp. The light in this came from white-hot lime heated by oxy-hydrogen gas. Through the spectroscope, this light showed the whole spectrum of colors. Each was pure and had no dark lines running down it.

Now he moved his sodium flame between the spectroscope and the lamp and looked again. There were two *D* lines there, all right—but they were dark.

The flame was somehow stopping the yellow light from the lamp at those parts of the spectrum.

Excited, he realized that this was no coincidence. The sodium atoms in the flame had stopped, or absorbed, light at the very parts of the spectrum where they usu-

ally sent out light.

"Because the sodium only absorbs the light at the two D lines, these dark lines identify sodium just as well as their bright counterparts," he noted.

Now the precise Kirchoff started checking whether other chemical elements also showed this duplicate code of dark lines. And he found that in each case, as long as the light behind was bright enough, they did. On December 15, 1859, he sent the news of his discovery to the Berlin Academy.

Once he had come this far in explaining the meaning of the dark spectral lines, Kirchoff also began to understand why the dark lines exist in sunlight.

"They exist because sunlight is not pure," he argued. "Somewhere on its journey to us, parts of the sun's light are absorbed, leaving dark lines in the spectrum."

But what could be soaking up parts of the sunlight in this way? Arguing from his experiments with the bright lamp and the dimmer sodium flame, he reasoned that the bright sunlight must pass through some dimmer vapor before reaching us. And because there are so many dark lines he felt sure that this vapor must be full of different chemical elements.

But where were these elements? They were not in space. And then the truth flashed upon him: they were in the Sun itself.

"The Sun must be a gigantic chemical factory!" he exclaimed. "And its outside must be less bright than its inside; so the outside absorbs the light that comes from the inside."

Exultantly, Kirchoff realized that he had found a marvelously accurate way of analyzing the Sun. Sitting quietly in his laboratory in Heidelberg, he could probe delicately and surely into the secrets of a vast mass of gas burning 93 million miles away!

With customary diligence, he began the laborious task of identifying the many dark-line spectra jumbled together in sunlight. Gradually he checked off one after another. Almost a celestial miner, he found metal after metal: sodium, iron, magnesium, calcium, chromium, copper, zinc, barium, nickel—all were there.

He went further: he made a beautifully detailed chart of the Sun's spectrum, drawing it all very carefully. He used three shades of crayon to portray different strengths of line.

In the middle of this painstaking, detailed work his eyes, which had been strained before, grew too weak for him to continue. He handed the remainder of the job over to a pupil named Hoffman.

When completed, the chart was nearly eight feet long and showed 2,000 separate lines. Yet, careful as it was, this chart had less than a tenth of the lines that a modern chart, made by photography, shows.

HUGGINS

KIRCHOFF had showed men how to analyze one star, the Sun. For William Huggins, a British amateur astronomer living at Tulse Hill, near London, this work was an inspiration.

"Here is a way to lift a veil that has never before been lifted!" he cried enthusiastically. "Now I will start to analyze the stars."

However, he knew that he needed to find out more about spectrum analysis before he could do this. Fortunately a friend and neighbor of his was an expert at spectrum analysis in the laboratory. The friend was William Allen Miller, professor of chemistry at King's College, London.

One winter night in January, 1862, Huggins went to hear Miller lecture on the subject in London. Afterward, the two men hired a cab to take them back to Tulse Hill. As their horse trotted through the quiet streets of London and out into the countryside, Huggins told Miller of his plans.

"You described Kirchoff's methods tonight," he said. "I would like to apply them to the analysis of starlight. Will you help me?"

"It sounds like a bold undertaking," replied his friend. "This is something I would certainly like to do."

By the time the four-wheeler pulled up at 90 Upper Tulse Hill, they had started making plans.

"Come in," said Huggins eagerly, "and look at my equipment."

Adjoining the house was his private observatory. It was a modest affair with a 12-foot dome and several fairly small telescopes. The best was an 8-inch refractor driven by clockwork, with a special object glass made by Alvan Clark, a great American lens maker.

"We can use this," said Huggins proudly. "But of course we need to fit a spectroscope to it. Do you have one that's suitable?"

Miller shook his head. "Nothing that will do for this job," he said. "No one has. We'll have to design one and get it made." He stared thoughtfully around the little observatory. "We'll have to identify the star spectra by comparing them with spectra of chemicals here on Earth," he added. "I'll rig up an electrical sparking apparatus to produce comparison spectra."

The two men quickly started designing and collecting the necessary apparatus. Huggins, who was a wealthy bachelor, spent his days running around London, bullying instrument makers. Miller came in triumphantly one day with an enormous induction coil and rows of batteries to give sparks. By creating sparks between different metals, he could get the spectra of those metals. These he could compare with the spectra in starlight.

At last everything was assembled and the Clark refractor, with the spectroscope at the eyepiece, was put into action. The bearded astronomer sat at the controls, and his friend took charge of the induction coil. For each star, they checked off lines by comparing them with one homemade spectrum after another.

To test their methods, they started with a quick general survey. They found that many metalic elements are definitely present in stars, just as they are in the Sun. On February 19, 1863, they sent a report of their preliminary results to the Royal Society.

The next project was to analyze one or two stars as completely as possible. They decided to concentrate on two prominent red stars, Betelgeux and Aldebaran, and a very bright star, Sirius.

Night after night they shut themselves up in the little observatory and strained to identify the faint spectral lines. It was a tremendously difficult job: the air is constantly quivering, and often the lines danced before their eyes until they felt like giving up.

However, they went doggedly on, peering into the spectroscope, sparking their comparison spectra, and then peering at the star spectra again. They also tried using the primitive photographic equipment then available, yearning to pin down the lines that flickered so tantalizingly before them. If they could take a photograph, they figured, they would be able to examine the star spectra at leisure. However, they had little success with this and had to keep relying on their eyes.

After a year's work, they had succeeded in identi-

fying a number of metals in each of their chosen stars. Betelgeux had five metals: sodium, iron, calcium, magnesium, and bismuth. Aldebaran had these too, plus tellurium, antimony, and mercury. Sirius had only three metals—sodium, iron, and magnesium—but they found hydrogen in it as well.

"Although stars vary in the elements they contain, they are all constructed on the same chemical plan as our Solar System," the two researchers announced in April, 1864.

Peering across billions of miles of space, they had found some of the very same elements that exist on Earth.

After this Miller went back to his laboratory at King's College, and Huggins worked on alone. At the end of August he decided to investigate a nebula. Astronomers were still not sure whether all these strange patches of light were really faraway star systems, or whether some of them were great clouds of shining gas.

Huggins realized that his spectroscope gave him a new way of finding out. Star systems would produce a complete spectrum full of dark lines. A shining gas would show a simple spectrum with only the bright lines for the gas.

Excited by his idea and full of awe, he turned his telescope toward a round nebula in the constellation of Draco.

All he saw was a single bright line. The nebula was a gas. Now he swung the 8-inch refractor toward the Great Nebula in Orion, one that Herschel had described as a hazy white spot. It, too, was gas.

"Could it be that stars gradually condense out of these great clouds?" wondered Huggins. If this were true, from his little observatory in London he might be looking at the birthplace of thousands of suns.

For Huggins, this was an inspired vision, but he could not prove that he was correct. Today, astronomers think that he was.

In the years that followed, Huggins went on to investigate other nebulae. By 1868, he had checked the spectra of another seventy. One third turned out to be masses of gas. The rest, however, had long, complicated star spectra; and so he knew that they were great systems of stars. He had proved that there were two kinds of nebula.

Using light, Huggins had succeeded in doing chemical analysis on a truly cosmic scale. But he knew that light carried another kind of message, too. In 1842 an obscure Austrian professor of physics named Christian Doppler had prophesied that the light coming from a star would be altered by the speed and direction of the star.

The kind of effect he had in mind occurs with sound, and the principles he established dealt primarily with sound. When we hear a change in the note of a train whistle as it rushes by us, the change is caused by the train's movement. The note of the whistle sounds shriller as the train approaches, and grows deeper as the train goes away. The reason for this is that sound moves in waves: long waves come from low sounds and short waves from high sounds. As the train moves nearer, the movement of the train pushes the waves forward and makes shorter waves and a higher sound. As the train moves away, the waves are pulled out longer, and the sound becomes lower. Doppler argued that if a star was moving fast enough, its light would change color for the same sort of reason. Today we know that at very high speeds this color change does occur.

At lower speeds there is no visible color change in the total light of the star, but there is a shift in the placing of the spectral lines. As a French physicist named Armand Hippolyte Fizeau pointed out in 1848, the greater the speed, the greater the shift. Here, then, was a way of figuring the speed at which a star was moving. Fizeau also said that the direction of the shift would depend on the direction of the star's travel. If the shift was toward the blue, the star would be approaching. A shift to the red would mean that the star was receding.

After his success with nebula, Huggins determined to try to measure spectral shifts. His first problem was to decide which was the best spectral line to use as a reference point.

To settle this problem, he wrote to James Clerk Maxwell, a great Scotch physicist for advice. Maxwell told him to concentrate on the F line of hydrogen.

And so in the spring of 1868 the indefatigable amateur turned his telescope toward Sirius once more. Gingerly, he adjusted the micrometer screws to register any shift in the F line. Hour after hour his attempt was baffled by tremors in the air that made the spectral lines waver. Hour after hour he struggled to keep the slit of the spectroscope, which was only 1/300 inch wide, trained exactly on the star. Although driven by clockwork, the telescope needed constant slight adjustment.

In spite of the enormous difficulties, eventually Huggins succeeded. The size of the shift was fantastically small, but it indicated an enormous velocity.

"Sirius is moving away at about 30 miles per second,

or over 100,000 miles an hour!" he proclaimed, his mind reeling at the idea.

He sent a note of this value to the Royal Society on April 23rd. Later he was to revise the value, bringing it down to about 20 miles per second. This is pretty much the modern figure.

Huggins went on measuring spectral shifts. He found that the stars were rushing around in a wild, random way; though they were called "fixed stars," and so they appeared to the naked eye, they were actually quite different in behavior, different even from each other. Some, such as Betelgeux, Rigel, Castor, and Regulus were retreating. Others, including Arcturus, Pollux, and Vega, were advancing. All were traveling at frightening speeds, though the speeds seem small because the stars are so far away.

Still trying to use photography, he struggled to record these shifts with a camera. At last, with the aid of improved techniques, he got a picture of the spectrum of Vega in 1876. Later, he managed to photograph many more spectra.

With the use of spectrum analysis, a new era began in the history of astronomy. Techniques of spectral photography were quickly improved. An American named Henry Draper recorded 78 different spectra between 1879 and 1882, and in 1886 Edward Charles Pickering and his co-workers at Harvard College Observatory began making a complete spectral survey of stars in the northern skies. By 1890 a new Harvard installation in Peru was being used to investigate the southern skies as well. Today, over 15,000 separate star velocities are known, and some 360,000 stars are cataloged according to the kind of light they emit. With spectrum analysis, it is possible to work out the chemistry of all these stars.

But the study of starlight was to do more than tell men about the chemical make-up of stars: it was to open up new ways of measuring the universe.

Until 1900, the only yardstick known to astronomers was parallax, the method used by Bessel. With it, the distances to some 5,000 stars had been painstakingly calculated. However, these were only a minute fraction of the visible stars. Also, they were all relatively close stars, because the parallax method could not be used on more distant ones. Astronomers were therefore seeking some way of gauging much greater star distances.

Finally in 1912 a clergyman's daughter named Henrietta S. Leavitt made a discovery that was to revolutionize distance measurements. It concerned some curious stars named cepheid variables.

SHAPLEY & HERTZSPRUNG

WEARING a high-collar blouse, and long skirt, Miss Henrietta S. Leavitt sat at her desk. Through the window she could see the low, ivy-covered buildings and four small domes of Harvard College Observatory. On the desk before her were piles of photographs and a low-power microscope.

She took up one of the photographs and placed it under the microscope. It showed a vast, ragged mass of stars; together they looked like a piece torn out of the Milky Way. This was the smaller of the two Magellanic Clouds. These clouds of dust and stars, only visible from the southern skies, had been photographed at the Harvard station in Peru.

Now she consulted a special catalogue of stars. It listed 1,777 stars of the kind called variable stars in the two Clouds. Intently, she searched the photograph until she found one of the listed variable stars. She estimated its brightness, noting the time when the photograph had been taken. Then she began hunting through other photographs for the same star at different times. Each time she found it, she noted its brightness and when it had been photographed. Slowly, very slowly, she built a picture of the way this strange star kept fading, brightening, and fading again.

A few years earlier, around 1908, another Harvard astronomer had been hunting variable stars. He was a lean, hawklike man named Solon I. Bailey. He had found lots of especially interesting stars in certain tight clumps known as globular clusters. He had identified the stars as a particular type of variable star, cepheid variables, named after a bright variable star in the constellation Cepheus.

"Most of the cluster cepheids change very quickly," he announced. "They go through a complete cycle in only about twelve hours. Some, however, fluctuate more slowly, taking twelve to twenty days."

No one knew why cepheids wink as they do. Nor did astronomers know the whole range of winking speeds. Miss Leavitt had decided to time those in the Magellanic Clouds.

Patiently she searched day after day for cepheids. One problem was that most of those in the Clouds were very faint, around the fifteenth magnitude. Long exposures were needed to photograph them, and many of her photographs did not show them at all. Also, there was a lot of obscuring dust in the Clouds, and so she concentrated on the smaller one, which was clearer.

At last, after months of careful work, Miss Leavitt

managed to work out the speed at which 25 of the 1,777 cataloged stars winked. Most of them took from a day to two weeks to complete the cycle from bright to dim to bright again.

Next she listed her figures, and placed the stars in order from the fastest winker to the slowest. Alongside the figures for each star she also put a note of the maximum and minimum brightness of each. And then she noticed something, something that made her sure she had stumbled on some secret of the cepheids.

The stars with slow cycles are brighter than the stars with fast cycles.

Excitedly, the young woman astronomer plotted a graph to show how brightness and winking speed were related. The result was a beautifully smooth curve. This proved that the link between brightness and winking

speed was no accident. However, it did not explain why the two were related.

In 1912, Miss Leavitt published her results. Although she did not know it, they were to provide a new way of measuring the universe.

In 1914, a young Missourian named Harlow Shapley was doing research at Princeton. His specialty was another kind of variable star, and he had just received his doctor's degree as a result of his work.

One day the director of Princeton Observatory, Henry Norris Russell, called Shapley into his study.

"Hale is coming on a visit from Mount Wilson," he said. "He wants to meet you."

The young astronomer was thrilled. George Ellery Hale had created some of the greatest observatories in the world. First he had established Yerkes, at Williams Bay, Wisconsin, with its big 40-inch refractor—still the world's largest. Then he had founded Mount Wilson, an observatory built high up in the clear air of Southern California.

When Hale met the young astronomer, he looked sharply at him through his glasses.

"I know of your work," he said abruptly. "I would like to have you join the Mount Wilson team."

To go to Mount Wilson meant using the best astronomical equipment in the world. Shapley needed no urging. With his wife Martha he packed up and made the long, slow journey across the continent. From Pasadena he went up the long, winding road that led at last to the peak of Mount Wilson, 5,714 feet above sea level. It was up this road, just 8 feet wide, that the parts of the giant 60-inch reflector had been painfully transported

seven years earlier.

When he came to the top he caught his breath at the beauty of the scene. There among the pine trees were the white derrick-like towers of Hale's solar telescopes, and the silver dome housing the great reflector. The air was pure and clear—clearer than any Shapley had seen back East. He gazed around, thinking of the marvelously clear nights of observing ahead. This was a dream observatory!

Shapley went on studying variable stars, but this time he chose to work on cepheids. With the 60-inch reflector, he could take photographs finer than any taken before. In particular, he could study the star spectra more closely.

Like Bailey, he concentrated on the rapidly winking cepheids in globular clusters. The 60-inch reflector revealed thousands of separate stars, opening up the clusters as no other telescope had. The great mirror gathered so much light that photography was speeded up. Shapley could get the spectrum of an eighth-magnitude star in 70 minutes and of a tenth-magnitude in four hours.

Night after night, as soon as the dome slid open, the stocky young astronomer climbed to the Newtonian focus near the top of the great telescope tube. There he guided the telescope for hours at a time while he took his photographs. Then, in the daytime, he pored over the results.

Soon he noticed a strange fact about the cepheid spectra. When a cepheid was at its brightest, the lines were shifted toward the blue. When it was dimmest, the lines were shifted toward the red.

Normally, spectral shifts mean a star is moving toward us or away from us. Blue shifts mean it is approaching, and red shifts mean it is receding. But the cepheids seemed to be doing both, rushing first one way and then the other. This did not seem possible.

Shapley puzzled over his problem, and then he had a brilliant idea. Maybe the stars were not actually moving to and fro, but their surfaces were moving in and out. Maybe they were constantly expanding and contracting.

"The spectral shifts would be the same," he said, struggling with the idea. "And yet . . . and yet . . ."

He figured that the gases at the surface of the stars would be rushing in or out at many miles per second. Some of the stars would change their diameter by as much as 10 per cent in a few hours. It was obviously ridiculous! And yet, what other explanation was there?

He went over the problem again and again, seeking some other explanation. At dinner in the observatory he hammered the idea out with other astronomers such as Adams, Seares, and Pease. Fantastic it might be, but his idea, they all agreed, certainly explained the observations.

Later a British astronomer and mathematician, Sir Arthur Eddington, took up the theory. He was able to calculate that it was possible for this extraordinary pulsing to go on without the star blowing itself to pieces. Today, astronomers know that cepheids do actually swell and shrink like this.

Meanwhile a Danish astronomer, Ejnar Hertzsprung, began to think that perhaps these winking stars could be used as distance indicators.

All astronomers knew that once the actual brightness of a star is known, its distance away can be determined by comparing its actual brightness with its apparent brightness. By the inverse square law, the amount of light reaching us from any star decreases in proportion to the square of the distance.

Studying Miss Leavitt's discovery of the link between the brightness of cepheids and their winking speeds, Hertzsprung saw that the winking speed of a star might be used to discover its real brightness. Once its real brightness was known, it would be easy to figure out how far away any particular cepheid was, by comparing the amount of light we see to the real brightness.

But how could he find the real brightness that went with any winking speed? The brightnesses noted by Miss Leavitt were the apparent ones as seen on Earth, not the real ones.

The only method he could devise was to start the other way around, and get the real brightness of some cepheids by measuring the distance to them. If the distance was known, he could calculate the real brightness by the inverse square law. This looked like an insoluble paradox: to use cepheids as distance indicators he had first to know the distance to the cepheids.

Fortunately, however, there was a way out of this difficulty. There are some relatively nearby cepheids and Hertzsprung could gauge the distance to these by another method. This method depended on a statistical analysis of how much these nearby stars seemed to move across the sky over the years. On an average, the nearer stars appeared to move more than the farther ones.

So the Danish astronomer hunted up the recorded movements of thirteen nearby cepheids and worked out how far away they were. Then he calculated how bright they really were by working back from how bright they seemed to be.

All the cepheids he was working on were fairly slow winkers, taking between 1.3 and 66 days per wink. He soon had the real brightness figures he needed for them. Since the cepheids studied by Miss Leavitt had much the same winking speeds, Hertzsprung was sure that he could transfer his brightness figures to them. This meant that he could figure out the distance to the Magellanic Clouds which she had studied.

The result came as a shock to everyone. At that time astronomers believed that our galaxy, which they took to mean the universe, was no more than 23,000 light years across. The Dane cheerfully came up with the fact that the Magellanic Clouds were a whole 10,000 light years farther away than they could be in a universe that size.

While astronomers everywhere were trying to understand what this meant, Shapley pounced on the idea of using cepheids as distance beacons.

"I will use them to find out how far away the globular clusters are," he decided.

The snag here was that, as Bailey had found, most of the cepheids in the clusters winked a lot faster than those used by Hertzsprung. However, by hunting around Shapley located some slowly winking cepheids in a few globular clusters. Hoping they were comparable to those used by Hertzsprung, he determined the distances to the clusters, and used these figures to calibrate the brightness of the fast winkers. Now he was ready to rule off the distances to as many globular clusters as he could see.

The results were staggering. Even a nearby cluster, M 13 in Hercules, was 36,000 light years away. The farthest went out to nearly a quarter of a million light years.

For these farthest clusters, however, even the great reflector did not always reveal individual cepheids, and so Shapley boldly switched to a new method. He compared whole clusters with each other and figured distances to the farther ones from his data for the nearer.

All this brought about a revolution in astronomical thinking, but Shapley had not finished. His next project was to use the globular clusters to map our galaxy. He believed that they were all a part of it.

Astronomers had already noted a strange fact about the clusters. Instead of being scattered all over the sky, most appear in the southern hemisphere. Further, one third are crammed together in a mere 2 per cent of sky, in the region of Sagittarius.

"It is unlikely that the clusters are really all bunched together," argued Shapley. "It is more probable that they are evenly spaced around the galaxy and this bunching is just an effect of perspective."

If he were right, our Sun could not be near the center of the galaxy, as astronomers thought. Instead, it would be toward one side, creating a perspective effect. And the center of the galaxy would be where the bunching appeared, in the region of Sagittarius.

By 1917, Shapley had completed his work. He had studied 93 different globular clusters to arrive at his conclusions.

"Our galaxy is a disk 300,000 light years in diameter and 30,000 light years thick," he declared. "The center is in Sagittarius, about 50,000 light years away from us."

Today we know that Shapley was right in believing our galaxy is far larger than anyone before had dreamed.

He was also right in deducing that we are positioned near one rim.

However, his distances were too large. He did not know about interstellar dust, which dims the apparent brilliance of stars by absorbing some of the light. Consequently most of the cepheids appear to be farther away than they are.

Although our galaxy has shrunk as a result of new calculations, it is still very large. Still disk-shaped, and with a central swelling, it is now reckoned to be some 90,000 light years in diameter and 10,000 light years thick at its deepest point. Our Sun is about 27,000 light

How our galaxy would look edge-on if viewed by someone in outer space. It is surrounded by its globular clusters and has a dark disk of interstellar dust running through its middle. Our Sun is about two thirds of the way out from the center and looks just like any of the other one hundred billion stars in the galaxy.

years or about two thirds of the way out from the center. And there are another hundred billion stars in the galaxy to keep us company.

And what of other galaxies? Back in the 1780's William Herschel said that countless other "island universes" exist. However, when Shapley announced his ideas about our galaxy, astronomers were still not sure that the other galaxies did exist. The man who finally proved Herschel right was Edwin P. Hubble, another astronomer at Mount Wilson. But the universe he revealed was even more fantastic than the one imagined by Herschel.

HUBBLE

HIS TALL, vigorous figure silhouetted against the night sky, Edwin P. Hubble stood at the Newtonian focus of the 60-inch reflector. He was making sure that the great telescope was exactly trained on a faint clump of stars and nebulae while he photographed them. There was a brisk wind and he wore his military trench coat, a reminder of his recent Army days. As usual, a pipe was clenched between his teeth and sparks from it were flying out into the great dome.

At last he stepped back with a sigh of relief. The photographic plate was exposed.

"Seeing conditions are pretty bad tonight," said Milton L. Humason, who had been watching him. "I hope you get something on that plate."

"We'll soon know," said Hubble, and he carried the

plate off to the darkroom for developing.

When he came back he was jubilant.

"If this is a sample of poor seeing conditions, I shall always be able to get usable photographs with Mount Wilson instruments," he declared.

It was 1919 and Hubble had just started working at Mount Wilson. He was delighted with the marvelous equipment at his disposal. Not only was there the trusty 60-inch, but a new giant which Hale had created—the 100-inch reflector. Housed in a vast new dome, this machine weighed 100 tons and the mirror had taken six years to grind. Over thirty electric motors controlled every movement of telescope and dome. With three times the mirror area of the 60-inch, Hale knew that it should reveal secrets that the older telescope only hinted at.

To Hubble, these giant telescopes were vital. Only with them could he try to fulfill his great ambition—to explore the galaxies. He wanted to determine, once and for all, whether they were groups of stars in our star system or separate entities at untold distances away.

At this time the question of whether the galaxies belonged to our star system or not was being debated everywhere by astronomers. Although Huggins, and later workers, had proved that galaxies are great groups of stars, no one had been able to find out if they were truly separate systems. Some echoed Herschel, believing that each was a faraway system equivalent to our own Milky Way. Others thought these stars lay within the vast disk that Shapley had just measured. One definite fact was that most were either elliptical, like footballs, or spiral, like whirling pinwheels, apparently trailing curved arms of stars.

"The thing that will tell us most is their distance," noted Hubble.

But how was he to measure the distances to any of the strange, remote systems?

"Maybe I can use cepheid beacons in the same way that Shapley did," he mused.

He began by hunting for cepheids in a ragged-shaped system looking something like one of the Magellanic Clouds, and cataloged as NGC 6822. Night after night he probed this system with the 60-inch reflector, yearning for reliable photographs of even one or two cepheids.

By 1923 he had at last managed to pick out a dozen variable stars in the system. But he was cautious about

Many spiral galaxies look like whirling pinwheels. This drawing is from a photograph of galaxy M 101 in Ursa Major and only shows the brightest parts of the galaxy.

what kind of variable star they were. They looked like cepheids but he could not be sure that they were.

At this point Hubble decided that the 60-inch reflector was not adequate for the job. He had to have more light-gathering power. And so he turned to the great 100-inch.

Here, a spiral, designated M 31 and lying in Andromeda, caught his attention. On the very first good plate Hubble found two ordinary novae, or flaring stars, and a faint, eighteenth-magnitude star of a type that he could not identify. At first he thought it was another nova. However, after checking through a long series of old plates assembled at Mount Wilson he found to his delight that it was a cepheid.

"It takes a month to vary and has a real brightness of about 7,000 times that of our Sun," he noted. He had found his first marker beacon.

Figuring from the scale linking brightness and distance he soon had an estimate of how far away the great spiral was. The answer staggered him. The distance was about 900,000 light years.

This proved that the spiral was far, far outside our own Milky Way. As soon as other Mount Wilson astronomers heard of Hubble's discovery, they concentrated their work on the great galaxy. Relying mainly on long-exposure photographs with the 100-inch, they managed to locate 36 variable stars among the millions in the huge spiral. Of these, 12 were identified definitely as cepheids. Checking the brightnesses of these, they found that Hubble's distance estimate held good.

Meanwhile, Hubble returned to NGC 6822. This time, he located some definite cepheids. From these he figured that the system was 700,000 light years away.

Here, then, were two great star systems far beyond the confines of our own galaxy. And if these two were so far away, the other star masses must also be galaxies and must be equally far away. To prove this, he went on hunting cepheids. By 1926 he had spotted 35 of them in another great spiral, M 33. This turned out to be about 850,000 light years away.

Meanwhile an astronomer named V. M. Slipher had been working on spectral shifts at the Lowell Observatory in Flagstaff, Arizona. Like Huggins, he was interested in measuring velocities through spectral shifts. Unlike the British astronomer, however, Slipher wanted to find the velocities not of single stars but of great groups—the groups Hubble was now finding to be separate galaxies.

Slipher had begun his work fourteen years earlier, in 1912. Curiously enough, he had chosen to start with the same spiral in Andromeda that later gave Hubble his first success. Using a fast camera, Slipher pinned its spectrum down clearly and then measured the shift. It was toward the blue: the star system was coming nearer— and at what a speed! Slipher pored over the plate, hardly able to believe his result. But there it was: the galaxy was advancing at the frightening figure of 190 miles a second! (Not that we need worry about a collision: the Andromeda spiral will not get anywhere near us for over a billion years.)

By 1914, Slipher had measured the velocities for thirteen different star systems; and by 1923 the number was up to 41. Other observers had by this time added five more, but Slipher still had a near-monopoly in this field of research. As the number of galaxies for which he had figures increased, he saw that although M 31 in Andromeda seemed to be moving toward us, nearly every other system was moving away. And all were traveling at dizzying speeds—averaging about 375 miles a second, but in one case going as fast as 1,125 miles a second. No astronomer had dreamed that such speeds existed for large bodies in the universe.

Astronomers everywhere were interested in Slipher's findings, but Hubble was particularly interested. In 1929, Hubble measured the distance to 24 of the galaxies whose speeds Slipher had found. And he noticed a strange fact: the farther away the galaxies were, the faster they were receding from us.

What did this mean? Was it just coincidence or did it have some real importance?

Sitting in his home at San Marino, Hubble brooded over the problem. A cheerful fire blazed in the hearth, and a fine selection of dry flies was at his side. A keen fisherman, he was planning a fishing trip in the Rocky Mountains. But his mind kept slipping away from fishing, returning to the mystery of the receding galaxies.

He could find only one explanation. Yet he hesitated to adopt it, for it seemed to start so many more questions.

"It looks as if the universe is expanding," he told his wife, Grace, at last. "Why else should all the galaxies be moving away in all directions?"

His wife gazed at him as if he had gone crazy.

"Expanding?" she asked. "How can it? What is it expanding into?"

"I don't know," muttered Hubble. "But there is no other explanation that I can see."

To try to find out whether his guess was right or not, Hubble decided that a big program of research was needed.

"Slipher only used a 24-inch refractor," he told Humason when he next saw him. "Imagine what we could do with the 100-inch reflector."

The two men discussed the project with W. A. Adams, now director of the observatory in place of Hale. Adams was fired by their enthusiasm.

"I will allocate you every possible amount of time with the 100-inch," he told them. Everyone connected with the project felt that it was the most ambitious project astronomy had ever undertaken. It seemed as if they were reaching to the very edges of the universe.

Hubble's plan was to measure distances by various means right out to the farthest galaxies, and to check these distances against velocities obtained by Humason through spectral shift analysis. If his hunch about the expansion of the universe was correct, the velocities should go on increasing with distance.

To test his equipment, Humason began by checking the shifts in spectra for a few bright galaxies whose velocities were already known. Then he turned his equipment toward more distant stars. Slipher had gone out far, but the giant reflector would go 35 times farther.

To photograph the spectra, Humason made very long exposures, keeping the telescope exactly on target the entire time. He also had to watch for air turbulence that would shift the image unpredictably. The telescope's automatic drive was no help for this.

As he reached out farther and farther, the galaxies appeared fainter and fainter. Longer and longer exposures were required. Eventually he needed ten successive nights just to get one picture. Only a man as untiring as Humason could have kept at the job.

By 1935 he had measured 150 new velocities. They grew larger with every increase in distance. These distances were all independently checked by Hubble who used as his base the way apparent brightness diminished. Starting with a relatively nearby cluster of galaxies in Pegasus, traveling at a mere 2,400 miles per second, Humason ended with galaxies some 240 million light years away and receding at 26,000 miles a second, or about one seventh the speed of light.

"The velocity-distance relation seems to exist over an immense volume of space," wrote Hubble. "The universe definitely seems to be expanding."

However, like a good scientist, Hubble cautiously pointed out that everything hinged on the observed red shifts.

"Either these reveal velocities or they are caused by unknown principle of physics," he said.

As scientists normally do, Hubble preferred to explain the shifts with known facts if possible. And everything seemed to indicate that the shifts did indicate motion.

"If the universe is expanding," he wrote, "it may finally be possible to determine the nature of the expansion and the time at which the expansion began—that is to say, the age of the universe."

Today astronomers agree with Hubble that the universe seems to be expanding. In fact this expansion was predicted by Albert Einstein long before Hubble's work. We also know that it is even larger than Hubble supposed. Walter Baade has shown that there is more than one type of cepheid variable, and this means that Hubble's original marker beacons indicate greater distances than he figured. For this and other reasons, we now know that his distance estimates are between two and three-and-a-half times too small.

Whether we shall ever know the age of the universe is another matter. In trying to find out, astronomers are probing farther and farther into the recesses of the universe. For this, they now have an even larger light-gathering telescope, the 200-inch reflector on Palomar Mountain. So far, it has seen five billion light years into space and shown us galaxies fleeing away at 86,000 miles a second, or nearly half the speed of light. But today's astronomers also have an entirely new way of exploring the universe, one which can penetrate even farther than we can hope to see.

Strangely enough, the man who devised this new way was not an astronomer. In fact, most astronomers did not know of his work until long after he had accomplished a great deal. His name was Karl Jansky.

JANSKY & REBER

FIFTY MILES southwest of New York City, a lean, balding young radio engineer sat listening intently to a radio receiver, headphones over his ears. It was a fine evening in the summer of 1931. Through the window of the laboratory room in which he sat, he could see a 100-foot-long contraption of brass pipes and wood struts, looking like the framework of a long narrow house. It was creaking around and around like a weather vane on four old automobile wheels, driven by an old motor at the center. This strange device, which was really a large radio aerial, made one complete turn every twenty minutes. And every twenty minutes the young engineer frowned in bewilderment as he listened.

"There it is," he muttered. "The same weak, steady hiss!" It seemed to be going down in the west, along with the Sun.

The young engineer, whose name was Karl Guthe Jansky, tracked the mysterious noise across the sky until it went below the horizon about sunset. Then he wearily removed his earphones, put on his jacket, and left the hut.

Outside, the flat New Jersey countryside was already growing dark. Jansky cranked his car up, got in, and drove noisily off along the highway toward his home in Little Silver, New Jersey.

As he sped along, Jansky brooded over the mysterious noise. Storms, he knew, generated radio noise, but that noise was quite different from this. He had built his device to study storm static and had already proved that ferocious bursts of radio noise were generated by thunderstorms. He had listened to storms as much as 140 miles away. But the faint hiss he had heard today and other days was continuous; and it followed a set course across the sky instead of coming from all around like storm static.

"Whatever it is, it surely is not due to storms," Jansky muttered aloud. "And so far as I can tell, it seems to follow almost the same track across the sky as the Sun does. Maybe it *is* the Sun!"

When he got home he told his wife, Alice, that he believed he had been listening to radio noise coming from far beyond the Earth.

In the days to come, Jansky sat in his room in the laboratory and listened again and again to the faint hiss. It was so faint that few people would have bothered to listen, for it was hardly louder than the ordinary hum of the receiver. But Jansky, who was hunting for every possible source of radio noise for his employers, the

Bell Telephone Company, hung on to it like a bulldog.

"If it's so faint, why bother with it?" asked Harald Friis, Jansky's immediate superior. "After all, your job is to search out noise that will interfere with radio-telephone communication. That's what Bell Telephone is interested in."

Jansky had no good answer to this, but he went on listening. He was determined to locate the source of the noise, whether it mattered or not. He just wanted to know.

By now he was recording the hiss, not as sound but as a wavy line traced out on hundreds of feet of moving chart. And after a while he realized, with mounting excitement, that it was starting earlier every day. It came up over the horizon before the Sun. This meant it could not be the Sun, after all.

Because his radio noise got up earlier, Jansky got up earlier, too. Before long he was getting up in the middle of the night to go over to the laboratory at Holmdel and track the hiss.

Then, as he yawned over his charts early one day, he noticed something which, although he could not explain it, was obviously important. The hiss started up exactly four minutes earlier each day. In a month, it gained two hours.

"What is it that comes up over the horizon four minutes earlier each day?" the puzzled engineer asked himself.

No one at the laboratory could help him, so he went to the nearest library and searched through books on astronomy.

His reading told him that the spinning of the Earth on its axis makes the Sun appear to go around it once every 24 hours. He also read that although we turn once in 24 hours in relation to the Sun, we turn a little more in relation to the stars. The movement of the earth on its orbit around the Sun creates the difference. After one year, this causes an additional complete rotation in relation to the stars. We turn 365 times a year in relation to the Sun, but 366 times in relation to the stars.

This meant that the stars rose and set more quickly than the Sun. Jansky feverishly jotted down the figures. If an ordinary day of 24 hours was 1/365 of a year, how long was 1/366 of a year?

The calculation was easy. The "star day" came out at 23 hours and 56 minutes instead of 24 hours—just four minutes less. Jansky had found his four minutes!

"The mysterious hiss is coming from the stars," he announced back at the laboratory.

Now he eagerly began to try narrowing down the area of sky from which the radio noise came. His rotating aerial could detect the east-west movement of the source of the hiss, but the aerial was not much good at gauging the altitude. However, after months of work he finally decided on two likely areas.

"The radio waves may be coming from the center of the Milky Way, or from the constellation of Hercules," he wrote in the spring of 1933.

His announcement caused a sensation. Newspapers and magazines reported his work, and the strange hiss was broadcast to the nation from a radio station in New York City.

"Our broadcast tonight will break all records for long distance," the announcer told his audience. "We shall let you hear radio waves from somewhere among the stars."

But it was a disappointment. This voice of the stars was just like the hiss of steam escaping from a radiator.

The New Jersey engineer wanted to go further. He even dreamed that he might build a great dish-shaped antenna 100 feet across to use for short-wave studies. However, his employers saw little practical benefit in such ideas and so, in April, 1937, Jansky reluctantly abandoned his research.

Professional astronomers were mostly skeptical about what he had achieved.

"It is hard to believe," they said. "Billions and billions of kilowatts would be needed to produce even the feeble effects noted by Dr. Jansky."

Fortunately, however, Jansky's results fired the imagination of at least one man. This was a radio ham living in Wheaton, Illinois; his name was Grote Reber.

Soon after Jansky had to give up his research, Reber promised himself that he would build his own antenna.

Each morning Reber drove into Chicago, thirty miles away, to design home radio receivers for a local radio company. But in the summer of 1937, as he sat at his drawing board, he began designing a very different sort of receiver.

"About 30 feet across," he decided, drawing out a great dish shaped something like a parasol.

It even had four spokes—very short ones—that met in the hollow over the center of the dish. Where they met, the radio waves would be focused by the dish. This was the collector, and a cable from it would carry the signals to his control room.

The control room was not as grand as it sounded—it was his cellar. Once the dish was planned, he had only to figure out how he could control its movement so he could study the portion of sky he wanted to study.

"The rotation of the Earth will swing it from east to west," he told himself. "So I only need to tilt it up or down."

To do this, he devised two semi-circular tracks to be placed under the dish, standing up like horseshoes, one on each side.

Once the device was planned, he had to get the apparatus off the drawing board and into operation. He ordered over forty pieces of galvanized sheet iron from a startled supplier, and demanded that they be cut to special shapes and numbered in sequence. He also got wooden struts cut out and fitted.

Working through the hot summer evenings, he

began assembling the pieces in his yard at home. Neighbors stopped to see what was going on, craning their heads over the fence at the great dish that was beginning to rise above the trees. But Reber was unperturbed, and by August he had finished. His radio telescope was ready.

The first evening after it was finished, he dashed home from work and went right to the cellar. But although he sat for hours with the headphones clamped to his ears, he heard nothing. It was a great disappointment.

He went on listening, day after day. And day after day the result was the same.

"Maybe the apparatus isn't sensitive enough," he said, worried, and he checked his calculations again. "Maybe with a better amplifier. . . ."

But better amplifiers did not help. And yet he knew radio waves must be bouncing off his dish all the time! It was exasperating.

At last he decided to try tuning to longer waves.

Jansky had listened in on the band of wave lengths between 14 and 20 meters. Reber had been trying to receive waves of only $3\frac{1}{2}$ inches, or about 200 times shorter. Now he retuned the apparatus and settled down once more in his cellar. But he still heard nothing.

Desperately, Reber began tuning to longer and longer waves. From $3\frac{1}{2}$ inches, he went to 13 inches; and then to over 2 feet, over 3 feet. . . . And one night in October, 1938, he tuned in desperation to 6-foot waves. As he switched the receiver on that night, he saw at last the sight he had almost given up hoping for. The needle on his meter was swinging across the dial.

"A signal!" he cried, grabbing his earphones.

All night he listened, with a contented smile on his face. It was the beautiful hiss he had dreamed of for so long.

Now the young engineer gave up all of his nights to listening. He came home from work, had dinner, and slept until midnight. Then he took his readings. At six in the morning he reluctantly emerged from his cellar, had some good strong coffee, and drove off to work. Instead of seeing the rich black farmland around him as he drove, his mind saw only traces drawn on paper, charts of unknown universes that he was beginning to explore.

But he had to know more about astronomy. He was getting plenty of records now, but he did not know how to interpret them. And so he enrolled at the University of Chicago and there began to study astrophysics.

When he could begin to interpret the maps and charts he had made, he took them to astronomers at Yerkes Observatory.

"Each line indicates a definite signal intensity," he said, spreading out a map that looked like a series of contours for height above sea level.

Otto Struve, the director of the observatory, pored over the drawings.

"Very interesting," he muttered. "Quite remarkable!"

"These seem to confirm Jansky's work," Reber went in excitedly. "See the rise in intensity here? This indicates exactly when the Milky Way passed over my arerial!"

Struve called in a young astronomer from Holland named Gerard Kuiper and asked him to take a look. Then other Yerkes astronomers came in. Everyone wondered what could be sending out such powerful radio waves. They knew of no mechanism inside the stars that would produce such waves.

"And what are these violent wiggles?" asked Kuiper hopefully, pointing at some tracings of signal strength.

Reber laughed. "A dentist three blocks away! Every time he starts drilling, I pick up static from the motor of the drill. Traffic is just as bad: the waves from their ignition systems is murder. That's one reason for starting my recording after midnight—there's less traffic around."

In 1940 Reber published his first results. Then, hoping to track down definite emitters of radio waves, he aimed his dish at some bright, nearby stars. He selected

Vega, Sirius, Antares, Deneb, and the Sun. To his surprise, he heard nothing from any of them. Not until four years later did he manage to detect a faint radio noise coming from the Sun.

Meanwhile he went on refining his radio contour maps. He discovered that certain areas contained especially strong broadcasts.

"One is toward the center of our galaxy, in the direction of Sagittarius," he wrote in 1944. "Others seem to be placed in arms projecting from our galaxy—perhaps in spiral arms of the type seen in other galaxies."

This was as far as he could go at the time. Today we know that his hunch about the spiral arms is correct. Radio astronomers have found that our galaxy is indeed a spiral. In fact it looks very much like the great galaxy in Andromeda, which is our nearest neighboring galaxy. We now know that the radio waves in the arms come mainly from gas between the stars, instead of from the stars themselves, but the powerful waves from the center of the galaxy are still a mystery.

Other sources of radio waves have also been located. Certain stars, apart from the Sun, are known to be radio emitters. And clouds of excited gas, probably left after the explosion of a star, also send out waves.

Other galaxies broadcast, too. Normally they are fairly quiet, like our own galaxy. The Andromeda galaxy is one of these. But there are some very loud galaxies, which astronomers call "peculiar" galaxies. The first of these to be identified through an ordinary telescope was Cygnus A, the second-loudest source of noise in the sky. Its appearance amazed astronomers everywhere.

SMITH & BAADE

The radio noise in Cygnus was originally noted by Grote Reber. Later three Englishmen named Stanley Hey, S. J. Parsons, and J. W. Phillips made a more accurate map of it by using longer wave lengths. They found it was concentrated in a small area which they called Cygnus A.

However, this area still covered a good deal of sky. Optical astronomers who looked at the area found it peppered with objects: some were nearby stars; others, distant galaxies. They could not pick out which of all these was the radio emitter. How, then, could this powerful radio source be identified?

At this point Martin Ryle, the director of the Mullard Radio Astronomy Observatory near Cambridge, England, decided that more accurate radio telescope was needed. "Maybe an interferometer will do the job," he said one day.

Ryle specialized in interferometers. Some were made up of twin antenna and the signals gathered by both are combined for the final reading. This system of two antenna makes an interferometer a more effective device than a single aerial. Also, the twin antenna are particularly good direction finders. If signals from a radio source arrive simultaneously at each antenna, this proves the source is the same distance from each, between the two. If the source is a trifle to one side, however, the signals do not arrive simultaneously and this immediately shows up on the record.

Among his interferometers, Ryle had two steerable dishes 27 feet across. These had once been used for radar

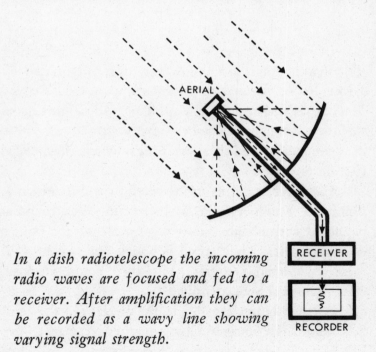

In a dish radiotelescope the incoming radio waves are focused and fed to a receiver. After amplification they can be recorded as a wavy line showing varying signal strength.

detection. Now they were set up 1,000 feet apart on an unused rifle range out in the countryside. Together, they made an especially exact instrument.

With these, Ryle thought he might be able to track down the exact position of Cygnus A.

Another member of the Cambridge team, Graham Smith, was very much interested in locating radio sources. He now took on the difficult job of trying to pinpoint Cygnus A.

In August, 1951, the twin antenna were turned toward a tiny area of sky. Sitting inside the yellow brick control building, Smith watched as their recordings were automatically written out by a machine. A wavy line was traced on a roll of paper emerging from the device.

Outside, farmers were hard at work gathering the harvest. The putter-putter of their tractor engines came in through the open window. However, the engines did not affect radio reception because the Cambridge astronomers had fitted suppressors to them.

Larger and larger waves were traced out as the signals grew stronger. Smith ran his hand through his thick fair hair and crouched eagerly over the paper. Hour after hour, the source of the noise crept nearer and nearer to the central position between the two antenna. Agitatedly Smith wiped his glasses and peered harder. He wanted to see the precise point at which the signals were strongest.

The moment came when he was not sure whether the waves were still getting larger. Then he was sure: the peak had been passed. Cygnus A had crossed over the center point between the two dishes.

He got up and raced along the corridor to Ryle's

office. The thin, taut figure of the astronomer was hunched at his desk.

"Martin, I've got it!" Smith exclaimed. "Come and look at the recording."

Ryle jumped up and followed the other man back to his room. The recorder was still working away, steadily feeding out its paper. Ryle picked up a length and looked along it. The peak showed up splendidly.

"This gives a really exact position," he said, and smiled with pleasure. "Graham, we can ask Baade to look for the source with the 200-inch."

On table-top Mt. Palomar in Southern California, a great silver dome 137 feet across stands up into the blue sky. It houses Hale's crowning masterpiece, the 200-inch reflector. Costing 6 million dollars and weighing 140 tons, it is the biggest light-gathering telescope in the world. The tube is so large that the observer can sit in a cage at the top *inside* the tube, and still let enough light by for the great mirror below!

Astronomers using this telescope live down in Pasadena and await their turn at observing. One of them, Walter Baade, had long been interested in radio sources. At the end of August he came into his office at the Mt. Wilson observatory, and found a flimsy airmail letter on his desk. It was from Graham Smith.

Baade tore it open, scanned it, and whistled softly with surprise. Then he went to a neighboring office where his friend Rudolph L. Minkowski was at work.

Together the two men studied the letter.

"This is the most exact position anyone has gotten," Minkowski said. "Are you going to look for it?"

"It's worth trying," declared Baade. "I'll see if I

can fit it in during my next trip to Palomar."

It was September 4th when his next chance to use the great telescope came up. That afternoon he said good-by to his wife Johanna and drove the 125 miles to the observatory. It would be his home for ten days.

At sunset, the dome, closed during the day to protect the mirror from the Sun's heat, slid open. Baade rode a little elevator to a deck running around the inside of the dome's base, and then stepped onto a moving platform that carried him up to the mouth of the telescope tube. It was tilted to one side of the dome so that he could get in from the platform. Now the elderly astronomer let himself down gradually into the five-foot wide cage. Here he would spend the night, taking photograph after photograph. As always, he was formally dressed in jacket and tie for his meeting with the stars. He was also as tense as a runner at the starting line, determined to achieve the most he could in the time available.

It was a perfect night. As Baade sat in the great telescope, an assistant below set it swinging silently away from the platform. It stopped, and then the assistant carefully aligned it on Baade's first target for that night. This was the Andromeda galaxy, which he was studying closely in order to revise Hubble's cepheid distance scale.

For several hours, Baade methodically went through his arranged program. And then, just before midnight, he was able to fit in the Cygnus work. The great telescope was trained on the exact position where the noise source should be in accordance with the location given by Graham Smith. Baade took two photographs.

The next afternoon, he developed the prints in one

of the observatory darkrooms. As soon as he saw the negatives, he knew that he was looking at something unusual. There were galaxies all over the picture—more than two hundred—but the one in the very center was unlike any Baade had ever seen before.

It had a double nucleus. And there seemed to be some distortion, as though there was an abnormal gravitational pull.

Baade brooded over the picture on his way to dinner that night. What did this strange double shape mean? Did it fit in with the purely theoretical study he had made earlier in the year? With a Princeton astronomer, Lyman Spitzer, he had tried to work out what would happen if two galaxies collided. Such a collision would be very unlikely, they had agreed; but it was not impossible. Maybe this was a picture of just such a collision!

That night he looked once again at the pictures before entering the observing cage. He wanted to fix them in his mind and think about them. All night he pondered as he went on with his routine work. And the more he thought, the more he was convinced he was right.

Back at Mount Wilson, Baade told Minkowski of his idea. Minkowski removed his glasses, looked quizzically at Baade, and then put his glasses back on his nose.

"No, Walter, I can't agree," he said finally. "The trouble is that you and Spitzer have been dreaming about colliding galaxies. Naturally you want to see them. But what proof do you have that that's what these blobs of light really are? Absolutely none!"

Baade was discouraged. He sounded out other astronomers, and they agreed with Minkowski. With a sigh, he let the idea drop.

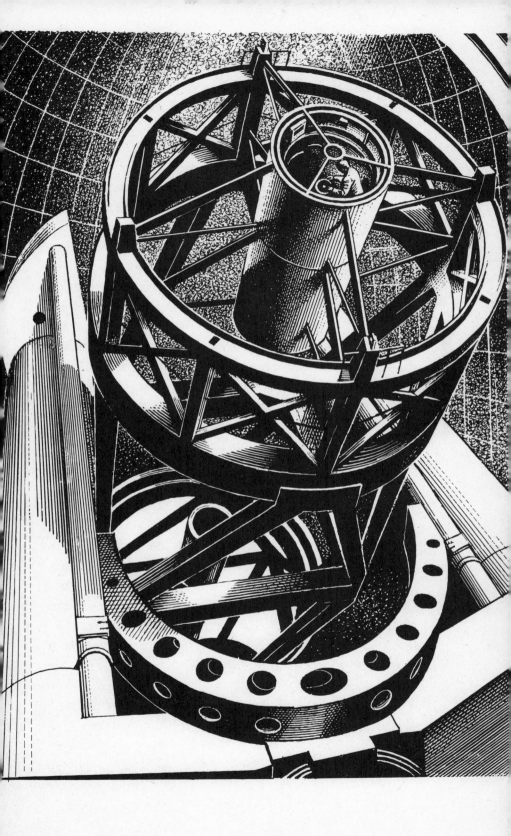

But he did not forget it. Nor did others let him forget it. Some six months later, he heard Minkowski making fun of it at a seminar.

"Bet you a thousand dollars I'm right," Baade said sturdily.

Minkowski laughed. "Walter, I can't afford a sum like that! Apart from everything else, I've just bought a house."

"All right, a case of whisky," Baade persisted.

Minkowski shook his head. "Not even that."

Eventually the two men settled for a single bottle. But how could they prove whether Baade was right or not?

"If the galaxies are really colliding, the interstellar gas will be terribly excited," said Minkowski. "Probably there would be neon V; the activity would have stripped off the outer electrons of the neon atoms."

"Then that's the test," declared Baade. "If neon V is there, it will show up on the spectrogram. You can photograph that at Mount Wilson."

Minkowski agreed to do the tricky job. A few weeks later, in May 1952, Baade was sitting in his office when Minkowski walked in.

"What brand shall it be?" he asked, and from the crestfallen look on his face Baade knew that he had won.

Minkowski brought his spectral photograph out. On it the thick dark line indicating neon V stood out clearly. It looked as if Baade was right: a fantastic collision had taken place 700 million light years away, and they were witnesses to it.

Today, astronomers are not so sure. The strange object in Cygnus may be a pair of colliding galaxies, but other explanations are possible. One is that a single galaxy is splitting into two parts. Another is that a galaxy is breaking up after a violent inward collapse.

What is certain is that the radio waves are not coming from the visible areas, but from two great wing-shaped haloes, going out about 100,000 light years. This has been discovered in England by two Jodrell Bank astronomers, Roger Jennison and Morinal K. Das Guptal. Why these haloes exist is a mystery.

Many galaxies with such double radio haloes are now known. They do not look especially alike, but they all send out tremendously powerful radio waves. Astronomers call them "peculiar" galaxies, because they are evidently quite different from ordinary galaxies like our own.

Today, radio astronomers are trying to find out just why peculiar galaxies exist. If they eventually find the answer, we shall know a lot more about the nature of galaxies and about the universe itself.

EPILOGUE

As we look farther and farther into space, we look farther and farther into the past. The 200-inch reflector has revealed a cluster of galaxies in Boötes, five billion light years away. We see these galaxies with light that has taken five billion years to travel from them to us. This means that it began its journey at about the time our Earth was born. We are looking at a part of the universe as it was then.

Some men believe that the universe is changing, or evolving. They believe that at some time in the past, perhaps some ten billion years ago, all the material that now forms the galaxies was close together, and that since then it has been flying apart and aging.

Others believe that the universe is, on the average, the same all the time. Although it is expanding, and galaxies are rushing away in all directions, more galaxies are being created as well. Ten billion years from now, they declare, the universe will look just as it does now. If they are right, there was no beginning to the universe and there will be no end.

By finding out what the universe was like in the past, we can try to judge whether or not it has been changing. Our telescopes are time machines for visiting different epochs. But so far we have not been able to go back far enough to find definite changes.

In reaching out farther and farther we cannot use light. The light coming from very distant galaxies is so faint that it cannot even be photographed. However, some galaxies emit radio waves much more strongly than they emit light waves. If the "peculiar galaxy" in Cygnus were ten times farther away than it is, optical telescopes would not reveal it but radio telescopes could easily record it. Thus, it is with radio waves that astronomers expect to explore the still farther reaches of the universe. By recording how galaxies were when the universe was much younger, they hope to find out whether there is any answer to the greatest question in astronomy: How did the universe begin?

For Further Reading

I hope that reading this book has made you want to find out more about astronomy and astronomers. Some books about astronomers which you could try are:

KNIGHT, DAVID C. *Johannes Kepler and Planetary Motion.* (Franklin Watts, 1962.)

MARCUS, REBECCA. *Galileo and Experimental Science.* (Franklin Watts, 1961.)

MOORE, PATRICK. *Isaac Newton.* (G. P. Putnam's Sons, 1958.)

RICHARDSON, ROBERT S. *Astronomy in Action.* (Whittlesey House, 1962.)

Some books about astronomy:

ADLER, IRVING. *The Stars: Stepping Stones Into Space.* (John Day, 1956.)

ASIMOV, ISAAC. *The Kingdom of the Sun.* (Revised Edition. Abelard-Schuman, 1963.)

BRANLEY, FRANKLYN M. *Experiments in Skywatching.* (Thomas Y. Crowell, 1959.)

——— *The Nine Planets.* (Thomas Y. Crowell, 1959.)

CHAMBERLAIN, JOSEPH MILES and NICHOLSON, THOMAS D. *Planets, Stars and Space*. (Criterion Books, 1962.)

CROWTHER, J. S. *Radio Astronomy and Radar*. (Revised Edition. Criterion Books, 1961.)

FENTON, CARROLL LANE and ADAMS, MILDRED F. *Worlds in the Sky*. (John Day, 1962.)

FREEMAN, MAE and IRA. *Fun With Astronomy*. (Random House, 1953.)

GALLANT, ROY A. *Exploring the Universe*. (Doubleday, 1956.)

HABER, HEINZ. *Stars, Men and Atoms*. (Golden Press, 1957.)

MAYALL, NEWTON and MARGARET & WYCHOFF, JEROME. *The Sky Observer's Guide*. (Golden Press, 1957.)

MOORE, PATRICK. *Telescopes and Observatories*. (John Day, 1962.)

REED, W. MAXWELL. *Patterns in the Sky*. (William Morrow, 1951.)

SIMON, TONY. *The Search for Planet X*. (Basic Books, 1962.)

ZIM, HERBERT S. and BAKER, ROBERT H. *Stars*. (Golden Press, 1956.)

ZIM, HERBERT S. *The Universe*. (William Morrow, 1961.)

Index—Glossary

Adams, John Couch, 72-83, 109

Adams, W. A., 122

Airy, George Biddell, 72, 73, 75-6, 77, 79, 81

Aldebaran, spectral analysis of, 98

Alpha Centauri, 70

Andromeda, (M 31), 118, 120, 121, 134, 140

Antares, 134

antenna: A device that collects radio waves from distant sources. 129, see also interferometer; Jansky, Karl

Arago, François, 78, 81-2

arc: any part of a curved line or a circle; in astronomical measurements, the apparent distance between two points in space. 19

Arcturus, 101

Argelander, Friedrich, 69

Aristarchus of Samos, 5, 8

armillary: a large device made up of a pole positioned parallel to the Earth's axis, and a large ring, or sometimes several rings; used for determining and mapping positions and movements of stars and planets. 15

axis: an imaginary line passing through the center of a body; sometimes the imaginary line around which the body rotates. See planets, rotation of

Baade, Walter, 123-4, 138-142

Bailey, Solon I., 104

Barnard's Star, 83

Berlin Observatory, 80

Bessel, Friedrich Wilhelm, 60, 62-71, 102

Betelgeux, 88, 96; spectrum analysis of, 98, 101

Bologna, University of, 3

Bonn Observatory, 69

Boötes, 144

Bradley, James, 30, 65

Brahe, Tycho, 14-19, 21, 65

British Association for the Advancement of Science, 82-3

Bunsen burner, 88

Bunsen, Robert Wilhelm, 88

Capella, 88

Castor, 87, 101

centrifugal force: force that impels a body traveling along a curved path to move out from the center of the curvature.

Navin Sullivan

This is Navin Sullivan's second "pioneer" book. The first, *Pioneer Germ Fighters*, was published in 1962 and has been widely read and enjoyed.

Mr. Sullivan has a bachelor's degree from Cambridge University. He attended Cambridge on a scholarship as a result of his earlier academic attainments. His interests in science have been lifelong.

After his graduation from Cambridge, he went into technical journalism and later into technical and specialized editing. He has worked on general books, textbooks, and educational journals. At present he is editor of science books for George G. Harrap & Co. Ltd. in England.

In addition to his science books for children, Mr. Sullivan has published many stories of fiction in magazines both in England and in the United States.

10|05
5